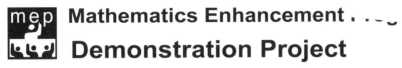

mep **Mathematics Enhancement . . .**
Demonstration Project

Practice Book: Y8B

Principal Author: Ted Graham, Centre for Teaching Mathematics, Plymouth University

Senior Editor: David Burghes, Centre for Innovation in Mathematics Teaching,
Plymouth University

Advisors: Graham Bryant   Caldicot Comprehensive School, Monmouthshire

Chris Graddon   Streetly School, Sutton Coldfield, West Midlands

Chris Hall   Hassenbrook School, Stanford-le-Hope, Essex

Malcolm Jenkin   Penair School, Truro, Cornwall

Mary Ledwick   Our Lady and St John High School, Blackburn

Graham Middleton   Stanchester Community School, Stoke-sub-Hamdon, Somerset

Adrian Smith   Penair School, Truro, Cornwall

Typesetter: Liz Holland

Checkers: Nigel Oates, Albine Patterson, Yanming Wang

This is one component of MEP Mathematics resources for Y8.

All enquiries regarding these resources should be addressed to

Mathematics Enhancement Programme
CIMT, Institute of Education
University of Plymouth   Tel: 01752 585346
Plymouth PL4 8AA   Fax: 01752 585344

First printing   January 2000

Published by **CIMT, Plymouth University**

Copyright © CIMT, Plymouth University

Design by *Clinton Banbury*
P.O. Box 2892, Billericay, Essex CM11 2LF
Tel: 01277 630421

Contents

12 Formulae

12.1 Substitution 1

In this section we practise substituting numbers for the letters in a formula: in other words, we replace the letters in formulae with their numerical values.

Example 1

If $a = 6$, $b = 3$ and $c = 7$, calculate the value of:

(a) $a + b$ (b) $a - b$ (c) $a + c$ (d) $c + b - a$

Solution

(a) $a + b = 6 + 3$
$$= 9$$

(b) $a - b = 6 - 3$
$$= 3$$

(c) $a + c = 6 + 7$
$$= 13$$

(d) $c + b - a = 7 + 3 - 6$
$$= 4$$

Reminders

We write: $2 \times a$ as $2a$

$a \times b$ as ab

$a \div 4$ as $\dfrac{a}{4}$

and $a \div b$ as $\dfrac{a}{b}$

Example 2

If $p = 6$, $q = 12$, $r = 4$ and $s = 3$, evaluate:

(a) rs (b) $4p$ (c) $2r + 3s$

(d) $\dfrac{s}{3}$ (e) $\dfrac{q}{s}$

Solution

(a) $\begin{aligned} rs &= r \times s \\ &= 4 \times 3 \\ &= 12 \end{aligned}$

(b) $\begin{aligned} 4p &= 4 \times p \\ &= 4 \times 6 \\ &= 24 \end{aligned}$

(c) $\begin{aligned} 2r + 3s &= 2 \times r + 3 \times s \\ &= 2 \times 4 + 3 \times 3 \\ &= 8 + 9 \\ &= 17 \end{aligned}$

(d) $\begin{aligned} \frac{s}{3} &= \frac{3}{3} \\ &= 1 \end{aligned}$

(e) $\begin{aligned} \frac{q}{s} &= \frac{12}{3} \\ &= 4 \end{aligned}$

Example 3

The perimeter of the trapezium shown is given by the formula

$$p = a + b + c + d$$

Calculate the perimeter if $a = 4$, $b = 6$, $c = 8$ and $d = 4$.

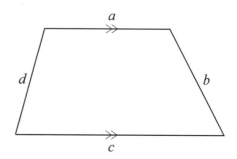

Solution

$\begin{aligned} \text{Perimeter } p &= a + b + c + d \\ &= 4 + 6 + 8 + 4 \\ &= 22 \end{aligned}$

Exercises

1. Calculate the values of the following expressions, if $x = 2$, $y = 5$ and $z = 9$:

   (a) $x + y$ (b) $x + z$ (c) $y + z$

   (d) $z - y$ (e) $y - x$ (f) $z - x$

   (g) $x + y + z$ (h) $z + y - x$ (i) $z - y + x$

2. If $p = 7$, $q = 2$ and $r = 3$, evaluate the following expressions:

   (a) $2p$ (b) $4r$ (c) $5q$

   (d) $5p$ (e) $6r$ (f) $2q$

   (g) $3p$ (h) $10p$ (i) $8r$

3. If $i = 6$, $j = 7$, $k = 3$ and $l = 4$, determine the values of the following expressions:

   (a) $2i + 3k$ (b) $2l + 3i$ (c) $2j + 5l$

   (d) $5j + 6k$ (e) $4i + 3l$ (f) $10j + 6l$

   (g) $3i - j$ (h) $4k - i$ (i) $6l - 2k$

   (j) $3i - 2j$ (k) $7k - 2i$ (l) $8l - 5k$

4. If $s = 10$, $t = 12$, $u = 15$ and $v = 20$, evaluate the following expressions:

   (a) $\dfrac{s}{2}$ (b) $\dfrac{t}{3}$ (c) $\dfrac{u}{5}$

   (d) $\dfrac{v}{10}$ (e) $\dfrac{v}{2}$ (f) $\dfrac{u}{3}$

   (g) $\dfrac{t}{6}$ (h) $\dfrac{s}{10}$ (i) $\dfrac{u}{1}$

5. If $e = 10$, $f = 20$, $g = 5$ and $h = 4$, determine the values of the following expressions:

   (a) eg (b) gh (c) ef

   (d) eh (e) $\dfrac{e}{g}$ (f) $\dfrac{f}{h}$

   (g) $\dfrac{f}{g}$ (h) $\dfrac{f}{e}$ (i) $\dfrac{e}{g}$

(j) efg (k) gfe (l) feg

(m) heg (n) $\dfrac{gh}{f}$ (o) $\dfrac{ef}{gh}$

6. In a sweet shop you can buy packets of mints for 20p each and bars of chocolate for 30p each. The total cost of m packets of mints and c bars of chocolate is given by the formula

$$T = 20m + 30c$$

   Use this formula to calculate the total cost if:

   (a) $m = 2$ and $c = 1$ (b) $m = 8$ and $c = 0$

   (c) $m = 3$ and $c = 3$ (d) $m = 5$ and $c = 4$

   (e) $m = 1$ and $c = 10$ (f) $m = 2$ and $c = 3$

7. The perimeter of the rectangle shown is given by the formula

   $$p = 2l + 2w$$

   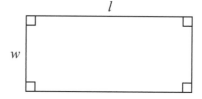

   Calculate the perimeter of rectangles for which:

   (a) $l = 2, \ w = 1$ (b) $l = 8, \ w = 2$

   (c) $l = 10, \ w = 9$ (d) $l = 10, \ w = 3$

8. The perimeter of the triangle shown is given by the formula

   $$p = x + y + z$$

   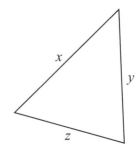

   Determine p if:

   (a) $x = 4, \ y = 8$ and $z = 6$ (b) $x = 2, \ y = 3$ and $z = 4$

   (c) $x = 10, \ y = 17$ and $z = 20$ (d) $x = 9, \ y = 14$ and $z = 15$

9. The cost of entry to a leisure park for an adult is £5 and for a child is £4. The total cost in pounds for a adults and c children is given by the formula

   $$T = 5a + 4c$$

   Calculate the cost if:

   (a) $a = 2$ and $c = 4$ (b) $a = 7$ and $c = 1$

   (c) $a = 1$ and $c = 5$ (d) $a = 2$ and $c = 3$

   (e) $a = 3$ and $c = 8$ (f) $a = 10$ and $c = 30$

10. The time, T hours, taken to drive D kilometres along a motorway at a speed of S kilometres per hour is calculated using the formula

$$T = \frac{D}{S}$$

Calculate the time taken if:

(a) $D = 200$ and $S = 100$ (b) $D = 160$ and $S = 80$

(c) $D = 360$ and $S = 60$ (d) $D = 5$ and $S = 10$

12.2 Substitution 2

In this section we look at substituting *positive* and *negative* values; we also look at more complex equations.

> *Reminder*
>
> **B** rackets
>
> **O**
>
> **D** ivision   **BODMAS** can be used to remember the order in which to carry out operations
>
> **M** ultiplication
>
> **A** ddition
>
> **S** ubtraction

Example 1

If $p = 2(x + y)$, calculate the value of p when $x = 3$ and $y = 5$.

Solution

$$
\begin{aligned}
p &= 2(x + y) \\
&= 2(3 + 5) \\
&= 2 \times 8 \\
&= 16
\end{aligned}
$$

Example 2

A formula states that $Q = uv - \dfrac{v}{4}$.

Determine the value of Q if $u = 8$ and $v = 12$.

Solution

$$
\begin{aligned}
Q &= uv - \frac{v}{4} \\[2mm]
&= 8 \times 12 - \frac{12}{4} \\[2mm]
&= 96 - 3 \\[2mm]
&= 93
\end{aligned}
$$

Reminders on adding and subtracting negative numbers

To *add a positive* number, *move to the right* on a number line.

To *add a negative* number, *move to the left* on a number line.

To *subtract a positive* number, *move to the left* on a number line.

To *subtract a negative* number, *move to the right* on a number line.

For example: $(-3) + 8 = +5$ (more usually written as 5)

$$7 + (-4) = 3$$

$$(-2) - 6 = -8$$

and $(-3) - (-9) = 6$

Reminders on multiplying and dividing negative numbers

The table shows what happens to the sign of the answer when *positive* and *negative* numbers are *multiplied* or *divided*.

× or ÷	+	−
+	+	−
−	−	+

For example: $3 \times (-7) = -21$

$(-8) \times (-11) = 88$

$12 \div (-6) = -2$

and $(-15) \div (-3) = 5$

Example 3

If $p = 9,\ q = -4,\ r = 2$ and $s = -7,$ determine the values of the following expressions:

(a) $p + q$ (b) $p - q$ (c) $q - r + s$

(d) ps (e) $\dfrac{q}{r}$ (f) $\dfrac{r}{q}$

Solution

(a) $p + q = 9 + (-4)$

$= 5$

(b) $p - q = 9 - (-4)$

$= 13$

(c) $q - r + s = (-4) - 2 + (-7)$

$= -13$

(d) $ps = 9 \times (-7)$

$= -63$

(e) $\dfrac{q}{r} = \dfrac{-4}{2}$

$= -2$

(f) $\dfrac{r}{q} = \dfrac{2}{-4}$

$= -\dfrac{1}{2}$

Example 4

If $a = 6$, $b = 5$ and $c = -2$, determine the value of:

(a) abc (b) $a(b + c)$ (c) $ab - bc$

(d) $\sqrt{a(b + 1)}$ (e) $\dfrac{ab}{2} + bc^2$

Solution

(a) $abc = 6 \times 5 \times (-2)$

$= -60$

(b) $a(b + c) = 6\left(5 + (-2)\right)$

$= 6 \times 3$

$= 18$

(c) $ab - bc = 6 \times 5 - 5 \times (-2)$

$= 30 - (-10)$

$= 30 + 10$

$= 40$

(d) $\sqrt{a(b + 1)} = \sqrt{6 \times (5 + 1)}$

$= \sqrt{6 \times 6}$

$= \sqrt{36}$

$= 6$

(e) $\dfrac{ab}{2} + bc^2 = \dfrac{6 \times 5}{2} + 5 \times (-2)^2$

$\qquad\qquad = \dfrac{30}{2} + 5 \times 4$

$\qquad\qquad = 15 + 20$

$\qquad\qquad = 35$

Exercises

1. Calculate:

   (a) $6 + (-2)$ (b) $(-3) + 5$ (c) $(-4) + (-2)$

   (d) $2 - 4$ (e) $3 - (-2)$ (f) $(-7) - (-4)$

   (g) $2 \times (-6)$ (h) $(-10) \times 5$ (i) $(-12) \times (-4)$

   (j) $(-8) \div 4$ (k) $14 \div (-7)$ (l) $(-25) \div (-5)$

   (m) $(-3)^2$ (n) $(-5)^2 \times (-2)$ (o) $(4 \times 5) + (-2)$

   (p) $(-3) \times (-4) \div 6$ (q) $(-3) \times (-8) + (-7)$

   (r) $\dfrac{(-6) \times (-4)}{(-12)}$ (s) $\dfrac{(-10)^2}{4}$

   (t) $(-3) \times (-5) \times (-9)$ (u) $(-5)^2 + (-6)^2$

2. If $a = 6$, $b = 3$ and $c = 7$, calculate:

   (a) ab (b) $b + c$ (c) $c - a$

   (d) $4b + 6c$ (e) $4c - 2b$ (f) $6a - 2c$

   (g) abc (h) $ab - bc$ (i) $2bc + ac$

   (j) b^2 (k) $a^2 - b^2$ (l) $a^2 + b^2 - c^2$

3. If $a = 2$, $b = -4$ and $c = -5$, evaluate:

   (a) $a^2 + b^2$ (b) ab (c) bc

   (d) $a - b$ (e) $c - b$ (f) $3a + 2c$

   (g) $2a - 4c$ (h) $3a + 2b$ (i) $ab - ac$

4. Calculate $\sqrt{a + bc}$ when $a = 15$, $b = 2$ and $c = -3$.

5. A formula for the perimeter of a triangle is $p = x + y + z$, where x, y and z are the lengths of the three sides. Calculate the value of p when $x = 1\frac{1}{2}$ cm, $y = 2\frac{1}{2}$ cm and $z = 3\frac{1}{2}$ cm.

6. The area of a trapezium is given by the formula
   $$A = \frac{1}{2}(a + b)h$$
   Calculate the area of the trapezium for which $a = 3$ cm, $b = 3.6$ cm and $h = 2.2$ cm.

   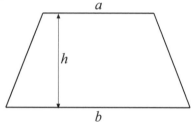

7. The length of one side of a right-angled triangle is given by the following formula:
   $$l = \sqrt{h^2 - x^2}$$
   Calculate the length l, if $h = 13$ cm and $x = 12$ cm.

8. The following formula can be used to convert temperatures from degrees Celsius (C) to degrees Fahrenheit (F):
   $$F = 32 + \frac{9C}{5}$$
   Calculate the value of F, if:

   (a) $C = 100$ (b) $C = 20$

   (c) $C = -10$ (d) $C = -20$

9. A formula states that
   $$s = \frac{1}{2}(u + v)t$$
   Calculate the value of s, if:

   (a) $u = 3$, $v = 6$ and $t = 10$ (b) $u = -2$, $v = 4$ and $t = 2$

   (c) $u = -10$, $v = -6$ and $t = 3$ (d) $u = -20$, $v = -40$ and $t = 3$

10. A formula states that:

$$f = \frac{u + v}{u\,v}$$

(i) Calculate the value of f, if:

(a) $u = 10$ and $v = 5$ (b) $u = 2$ and $v = 5$

(c) $u = 20$ and $v = 10$

(ii) Show that you obtain the same value in each case using the formula

$$f = \frac{1}{v} + \frac{1}{u}$$

Why does this happen?

11. Alan knows that $x = 2$, $y = -6$ and $z = -4$. He calculates that $Q = \frac{1}{4}$.

Which of the formulae below could he have used?

Formula A $Q = \dfrac{x\,y + y\,z}{x\,y\,z}$

Formula B $Q = \dfrac{y\,z - x\,y}{x\,y\,z}$

Formula C $Q = \dfrac{1}{x} - \dfrac{1}{z}$

Formula D $Q = \dfrac{1}{z} + \dfrac{1}{x}$

Formula E $Q = \dfrac{1}{x} + \dfrac{1}{y}$

12.3 Linear Equations 1

In this section we revise the solution of simple equations.

Reminder

Whatever you do to *one side* of an equation you must do to the *other side*: it is like keeping a set of scales balanced.

It is conventional to give the solution to an equation with the *unknown value* on the *left hand side*, and its *value* on the *right hand side*, e.g. $x = 4$ not $4 = x$.

Example 1

Solve the following equations:

(a) $x + 3 = 7$

(b) $13 = 5 + a$

(c) $y - 3 = 8$

(d) $11 = p - 4$

Solution

(a) $x + 3 = 7$

[Subtract 3 from both sides] $x = 7 - 3$

$x = 4$

(b) $13 = 5 + a$

[Subtract 5 from both sides] $13 - 5 = a$

$8 = a$

$a = 8$

(c) $y - 3 = 8$

[Add 3 to both sides] $y = 8 + 3$

$y = 11$

(d) $11 = p - 4$

[Add 4 to both sides] $11 + 4 = p$

$15 = p$

$p = 15$

Example 2

Solve the following equations:

(a) $6x = 24$ (b) $15 = 3t$ (c) $\dfrac{w}{2} = 9$

Solution

(a) $6x = 24$

[Divide both sides by 6] $x = \dfrac{24}{6}$

$x = 4$

(b) $15 = 3t$

[Divide both sides by 3] $\dfrac{15}{3} = t$

$5 = t$

$t = 5$

(c) $\dfrac{w}{2} = 9$

[Multiply both sides by 2] $w = 9 \times 2$

$w = 18$

Example 3

The length of the rectangle shown is 4 metres, and its width is x metres.

The area of the rectangle is 8 m^2.

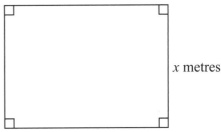

x metres

(a)   Use this information to write down an equation involving x.

(b)   Solve the equation to determine the value of x.

4 metres

(c)   What is the width of the rectangle in cm?

Solution

(a)   The area of the rectangle is $(4 \times x) \text{ m}^2$, and we are told that this equals 8 m^2.

So the equation is $4 \times x = 8$, which we write as $4x = 8$.

(b) $4x = 8$

[Divide both sides by 4] $x = \dfrac{8}{4}$

$x = 2 \text{ m}$

(c)   The width of the rectangle is 200 cm.

Exercises

1.   Solve the following equations:

(a) $x + 5 = 9$ (b) $x + 11 = 12$ (c) $7 + x = 9$

(d) $x + 2 = 17$ (e) $14 = x + 6$ (f) $x - 2 = 10$

(g) $x - 6 = 5$ (h) $2 = x - 9$ (i) $x + 3 = 0$

(j) $x - 7 = 7$ (k) $x + 12 = 7$ (l) $x - 6 = -10$

2.   Solve the following equations:

(a) $2x = 12$ (b) $3x = 18$ (c) $5x = 20$

(d) $7x = 21$ (e) $36 = 9x$ (f) $5x = 0$

(g) $80 = 10x$ (h) $\dfrac{x}{2} = 5$ (i) $\dfrac{x}{3} = 6$

(j) $9 = \dfrac{x}{4}$ (k) $\dfrac{x}{2} = 22$ (l) $\dfrac{x}{7} = 4$

(m) $4x = 2$ (n) $\dfrac{x}{2} = 6$ (o) $\dfrac{x}{10} = 0$

3.   Solve the following equations:

(a) $x + 7 = 9$ (b) $x - 6 = 8$ (c) $3x = 33$

(d) $\dfrac{x}{5} = 2$ (e) $x + 2 = 13$ (f) $5x = 35$

(g) $4 + x = 15$ (h) $7 = y - 9$ (i) $42 = 6p$

(j) $90 = \dfrac{q}{9}$ (k) $5r = -10$ (l) $-4 = \dfrac{s}{8}$

4.   The area of the rectangle shown is 18 cm^2.

(a)   Write down an equation involving x.

(b)   Solve your equation.

(c)   Write down the width of the rectangle.

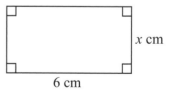

5.   The perimeter of the triangle shown is 17 cm.

(a)   Write down an equation and solve it for x.

(b)   Write down the length of the side marked x .

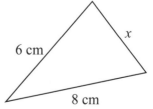

12.4 Linear Equations 2

In this section we solve linear equations where more than one step is needed to reach the solution. There are no simple rules here, since methods of solution vary from one equation to another.

Example 1

Solve the equation,

$$5x + 2 = 17$$

Solution

The first step is to subtract 2 from both sides, giving

$$5x = 15$$

Secondly, divide both sides by 5, to give the solution

$$x = 3$$

Example 2

Solve the equation,

$$4x - 7 = 17$$

Solution

[Add 7 to both sides] $4x = 24$

[Divide both sides by 4] $x = 6$

Example 3

Solve the equation,

$$5(7 + 2x) = 65$$

Solution

EITHER

[Multiply out the brackets]
$$35 + 10x = 65$$

[Subtract 35 from both sides]
$$10x = 30$$

[Divide both sides by 3] $x = 3$

OR

[Divide both sides by 5]
$$7 + 2x = 13$$

[Subtract 7 from both sides]
$$2x = 6$$

[Divide both sides by 2] $x = 3$

Example 4

Solve the equation,

$$6x - 2 = 4x + 8$$

Solution

[Subtract $4x$ from both sides] $2x - 2 = 8$

[Add 2 to both sides] $2x = 10$

[Divide both sides by 2] $x = 5$

Example 5

Solve the equation,

$$\frac{p}{2} + 3 = 7$$

Solution

EITHER   *OR*

[Subtract 3 from both sides] $\dfrac{p}{2} = 4$ [Multiply both sides by 2] $p + 6 = 14$

[Multiply both sides by 2] $p = 8$ [Subtract 6 from both sides] $p = 8$

Example 6

Solve the equation

$$\frac{p + 3}{2} = 7$$

Solution

[Multiply both sides by 2] $p + 3 = 14$

[Subtract 3 from both sides] $p = 11$

Exercises

1. Solve the following equations:

   (a) $3x + 2 = 17$ (b) $5x - 6 = 9$ (c) $6x - 4 = 8$

   (d) $3(x + 4) = 30$ (e) $5(2x - 3) = 15$ (f) $7 - 2x = 3$

   (g) $6x - 4 = 32$ (h) $6x + 7 = 1$ (i) $7x + 6 = 34$

   (j) $6x - 7 = 11$ (k) $2x + 15 = 16$ (l) $8 - 2x = 5$

   (m) $38 = 3y + 2$ (n) $35 = 5(7 + 2p)$ (o) $56 = 7(2 - 3q)$

2. Solve the following equations:

   (a) $\dfrac{x}{2} + 5 = 9$ (b) $14 = \dfrac{x}{3} - 8$ (c) $\dfrac{y}{5} - 9 = -2$

   (d) $\dfrac{z}{4} + 8 = 3$ (e) $7 = \dfrac{p}{4} - 6$ (f) $\dfrac{x + 5}{2} = 9$

   (g) $14 = \dfrac{x - 8}{3}$ (h) $\dfrac{y - 9}{5} = -2$ (i) $\dfrac{z + 8}{4} = 3$

   (j) $7 = \dfrac{p - 6}{4}$ (k) $\dfrac{2x}{3} + 1 = 9$ (l) $\dfrac{5x}{4} - 7 = 3$

3. Solve the following equations:

   (a) $2x + 3 = x + 10$ (b) $6x - 2 = 4x + 7$

   (c) $16x - 7 = 8x + 17$ (d) $11x + 2 = 8x + 7$

   (e) $x + 1 = 2(x - 1)$ (f) $3(x + 4) = 5(x - 2)$

   (g) $9(x + 7) = 2(5x - 7)$ (h) $3(2x - 1) = 4(3x - 4)$

4. The formula $F = 32 + \dfrac{9C}{5}$ can be used to convert temperatures from degrees Celsius (C) to degrees Fahrenheit (F).

   (a) Copy and complete the following solution to calculate the value of C when F is $86\,°$:

$$F = 32 + \frac{9C}{5}$$

[Substitute 86 for F] $\qquad 86 = 32 + \dfrac{9C}{5}$

[Subtract 32 from both sides] $\qquad =$

[Multiply both sides by 5] $\qquad =$

[Divide both sides by 9] $\qquad =$

$$C =$$

(b) Calculate the value of C when F is 41, using the process as in part (a).

(c) Calculate the value of C when F is 23.

5. The formula $p = 2(x + y)$ can be used to work out the perimeter of a rectangle with sides x and y. Use the same approach as in question 4, to set up and solve an equation to calculate the value of x, if $p = 50$ and $y = 8$.

6. A formula states that $v = u + at$. Set up and solve an equation to determine the value of a, if,

   (a) $v = 10$, $u = 3$ and $t = 5$,

   (b) $v = 2$, $u = 5$ and $t = 3$.

7. The perimeter of the rectangle shown is 16 cm. Calculate the value of x.

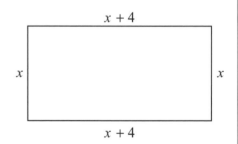

8. The perimeter of the triangle shown is 23 cm. Calculate the value of x.

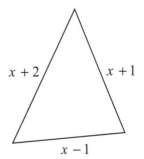

9. The area of the rectangle shown is 19.5 cm^2. Determine the value of x.

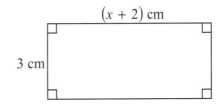

10. The following two rectangles have the same areas:

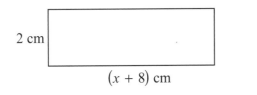 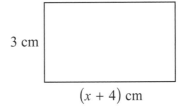

(a) Determine the value of x.

(b) Write down the lengths of the two rectangles.

12.5 Non-Linear Equations

Solutions to non-linear equations are not always possible with the methods we have been using for linear equations: sometimes it is necessary to use a method called *trial and improvement*, where you make a sensible first guess at the solution, and then you try to improve your estimate. The method is illustrated in the examples which follow.

Example 1

Solve the equation,

$$x^3 = 100$$

giving your answer correct to 1 decimal place.

Solution

If we substitute $x = 4$ into the expression x^3, we get $4^3 = 64$, which is *less* than 100.

If we substitute $x = 5$, we get $5^3 = 125$, which is *more* than 100.

This tells us that there is a solution between 4 and 5.

We now improve our solution. A good way to record the values that you calculate is to use a table, and to make comments as you go:

x	x^3	Comments
4	64	4 is *too low*
5	125	5 is *too high*: the solution is between 4 and 5
4.5	91.125	4.5 is *too low*
4.6	97.336	4.6 is *too low*
4.7	103.823	4.7 is *too high*: the solution is *between 4.6 and 4.7*
4.65	100.544625	4.65 is *too high*

From the table we can see that 4.6 is *too low*, and 4.65 is *too high*, so the solution is *between 4.6 and 4.65*.

So, we may write

$$4.6 < x < 4.65$$

The statement means that, when it is rounded, x will be 4.6 correct to one decimal place:

$$x = 4.6 \quad \text{(to 1 d.p.)}$$

Note If we need the solution to a greater degree of accuracy, then we continue the process and extend the table.

Example 2

Use trial and improvement to solve the equation $x^3 + x = 20$, giving your answer correct to 2 decimal places.

Solution

x	$x^3 + x$	Comments
2	10	2 is *too low*
3	30	3 is *too high*: solution is *between 2 and 3*
2.5	18.125	2.5 is *too low*
2.6	20.176	2.6 is *too high*: solution is *between 2.5 and 2.6*
2.55	19.131	2.55 is *too low*
2.58	19.754	2.58 is *too low*
2.59	19.964	2.59 is *too low*: solution is *between 2.59 and 2.6*
2.595	20.070	2.595 is *too high*

From the table we can see that the solution of x is between 2.59 and $2.595,$ so

$$2.59 < x < 2.595$$

When we round off, $x = 2.59$ correct to 2 decimal places.

Exercises

1. Use the trial and improvement method to solve the following equations for positive x:

   (a) $x^2 = 15$ to 1 decimal place,

   (b) $x^2 + x = 28$ to 1 decimal place,

   (c) $x^4 + 5 = 80$ to 1 decimal place,

   (d) $\dfrac{6}{x^2} = 0.1$ to 1 decimal place.

2. (a) Show that the equation $x^3 - x^2 = 2$ has a solution between 1 and 2.

   (b) Use trial and improvement to solve the equation $x^3 - x^2 = 2,$ giving your solution correct to 2 decimal places.

3. (a) Show that the equation $x^2 + 2x + 3 = 15$ has a solution between 2 and 3.

   (b) Use trial and improvement to solve the equation $x^2 + 2x + 3 = 15,$ giving your answer correct to 2 decimal places.

4. Use a trial and improvement method to solve $x^3 - 5x - 1 = 0$ for positive x, giving your answer correct to 2 decimal places.

12.6 Changing the Subject of a Formula

We say that v is the *subject* of the formula $v = u + at$.

The formula can be rearranged so that $a = \dfrac{v - u}{t}$, and we now say that a is the subject of the formula. When rearranging a formula you must use the same approach as when you solve equations.

Note When giving your solution at the end, remember to write the *subject* of the formula on the *left hand side* of the equation.

Example 1

Make x the subject of each of the following formulae:

(a) $y = x + 8$ (b) $y = 2x - 4$

Solution

(a) $y = x + 8$

[Subtract 8 from both sides] $y - 8 = x$

$x = y - 8$

(b) $y = 2x - 4$

[Add 4 to both sides] $y + 4 = 2x$

[Divide both sides by 2] $\dfrac{y + 4}{2} = x$

$x = \dfrac{y + 4}{2}$

Example 2

Make t the subject of each of the following equations:

(a) $v = u + at$ (b) $p = k(b + t)$

Solution

(a) $v = u + at$

[Subtract u from both sides] $v - u = at$

[Divide both sides by a] $\dfrac{v - u}{a} = t$

$t = \dfrac{v - u}{a}$

(b) $p = k(b + t)$

EITHER

[Multiply out the brackets]
$$p = kb + kt$$

[Subtract kb from both sides]
$$p - kb = kt$$

[Divide both sides by k]
$$\dfrac{p - kb}{k} = t$$

$$t = \dfrac{p - kb}{k}$$

OR

[Divide both sides by k]

$$\dfrac{p}{k} = b + t$$

[Subtract b from both sides]

$$\dfrac{p}{k} - b = t$$

$$t = \dfrac{p}{k} - b$$

Note that these two formulae are equivalent, even though they look different, because

$$\frac{p - kb}{k} = \frac{p}{k} - \frac{kb}{k}$$

$$= \frac{p}{k} - b$$

Exercises

1. Make x the subject of each of the following formulae:

   (a) $y = x - 2$ (b) $y = x + 7$ (c) $y = 4x$

   (d) $y = \dfrac{x}{3}$ (e) $y = 2x + 1$ (f) $y = 4x - 3$

   (g) $y = 2(x + 3)$ (h) $y = 3(x - 4)$ (i) $y = mx$

   (j) $y = x + a$ (k) $y = kx - c$ (l) $y = ax + b$

2. (a) Make a the subject of the formula $y = ax + b$.

   (b) Make b the subject of the formula $y = ax + b$.

3. If $y = \dfrac{3x - 7}{2}$, express x in terms of y.

4. The formula $F = 32 + \dfrac{9C}{5}$ is used for converting temperatures for degrees Celsius (C) to degrees Fahrenheit (F). Make C the subject of this formula.

5. The perimeter of the triangle shown is

   $$p = a + b + c$$

   (a) Make a the subject of this formula.

   (b) Make c the subject of this formula.

   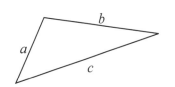

6. (a) Complete the following formula for the perimeter of the rectangle shown:

   $$p = 2w + \dots$$

   (b) Make w the subject of your formula.

   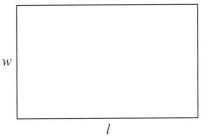

(c)   Complete the following formula for
       the area of the rectangle:

       $A = \ldots\ldots\ldots\ldots$

(d)   Make l the subject of your formula.

7. (a)   Write down a formula for the perimeter, p,
           of the shape shown.

    (b)   Make x the subject of your formula.

    (c)   Make l the subject of your formula

    (d)   Make b the subject of your formula.

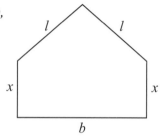

8.   The area of the trapezium shown is given by
      the formula

      $$A = \frac{h}{2}(a + b)$$

    (a)   Make h the subject of the formula.

    (b)   Make a the subject of the formula.

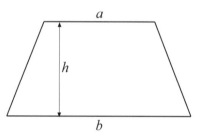

9.   Write down a formula for the perimeter of
      the shape shown, and then make x the
      subject of the formula.

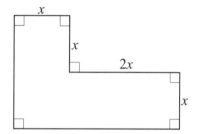

10. (a)   Write down a formula for the shaded
            area, A, in the diagram shown.

     (b)   Make x the subject of the formula.

     (c)   Make y the subject of the formula.

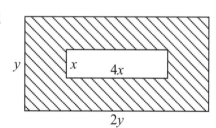

13 Money and Time

13.1 Money

In this section we revise basic arithmetic, working with *money*.

Example 1

(a)   What is the cost of 7 packets of crisps costing 24p each?

(b)   How much change do you get from £5 when paying for these crisps?

Solution

(a)   The cost of the crisps is found by multiplying 24 by 7.

$$\begin{array}{r} 2\,4 \\ \times \quad 7 \\ \hline 1\,6\,8 \end{array}$$

The cost is 168p or £1.68.

(b)   The change is found by subtracting £1.68 from £5.00.

$$\begin{array}{r} 5\,.\,0\,0 \\ -\ 1\,.\,6\,8 \\ \hline 3\,.\,3\,2 \end{array}$$

The change is £3.32.

Example 2

Joshua buys a cheeseburger costing £1.59, a portion of chips costing 99p and a drink costing £1.15.

(a)   How much does he spend?

(b)   How much change does he get from a £10 note?

Solution

We add the three amounts, remembering to change the cost of the chips from pence into pounds.

(a)

$$\begin{array}{r} 1\,.\,5\,9 \\ 1\,.\,1\,5 \\ +\ 0\,.\,9\,9 \\ \hline 3\,.\,7\,3 \end{array}$$

He spends a total of £3.73.

(b)   1 0 . 0 0
        −   3 . 7 3
        ─────────
            6 . 2 7

He gets £6.27 change.

Example 3

5 boys are paid £38.60 for clearing rubbish from a garden. They share the money equally. How much does each boy receive?

Solution

We divide the total amount earned by the number of boys.

$$
\begin{array}{r}
7.72 \\
5\overline{\smash{)}38.\!{}^{3}6\!{}^{1}0}
\end{array}
$$

Each boy receives £7.72.

Example 4

Mandy buys 8 'Candichoc' bars. They cost a total of £3.04. How much does each 'Candichoc' bar cost?

Solution

We divide the total cost by the number of bars.

$$
\begin{array}{r}
0.38 \\
8\overline{\smash{)}3.0\!{}^{6}4}
\end{array}
$$

Each 'Candichoc' bar costs 38p.

Exercises

1. Anthony pays £1.35 to swim at a sports centre. He then buys a drink costing 79p and a packet of crisps costing 27p from the sports centre café.

    (a) How much does he spend altogether?

    (b) How much money does he have left if he had £6.30 when he entered the sports centre?

2. A family buys 3 children's meals that cost £1.99 each and 2 value meals that cost £3.49 each. How much does the family spend altogether?

3.   Jamil wants to buy a bike that costs £249.99. He has saved £192.50. How much more does he need to save before he can buy the bike?

4.   A teacher buys a chocolate bar for each child in her class. The bars cost 34p each. There are 31 children in her class.

   (a)   How much does she spend?

   (b)   How much change does she get from a £20 note?

5.   A tutor group raises £86.28 for charity. They decide to divide the money equally between 4 charities.

   (a)   What amount do they give to each charity?

   (b)   How much extra would they have to raise for each of the charities to be given £28 ?

6.   Tickets for a school play cost £1.20 for children and £2.10 for adults. What would be the total cost of tickets for:

   (a)   2 adults and 4 children,

   (b)   3 adults and 2 children?

7.   If £40.92 is divided equally between 12 people, how much do they each receive?

8.   Three brothers divide £20 between them so that they each have exactly the same amount of money. A small amount is left over.

   (a)   What is the largest amount they can each receive?

   (b)   How much money is left over?

9.   Six children are given a sum of money. They divide it equally so that they each receive £8.33 and there is 2p left over.

   (a)   What was the sum of money they were given?

   (b)   If £5 of the money had been given to a charity, what amount of money would each of the children have received?

10.   Hannah wants to buy 12 bottles of lemonade for her birthday party. At her local supermarket, lemonade is on a *'buy one, get one at half price'* special offer. The bottles cost £1.18 each.

   (a)   How much does Hannah pay for the 12 bottles of lemonade?

   (b)   How much does she save because of the special offer?

13.2 Time

In this section we revise the use of the 24-hour clock and consider problems involving *time* and time *zones*.

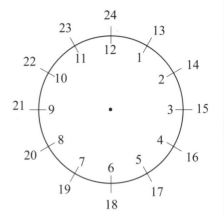

Example 1

Convert the following times to 24-hour clock times:

(a) 7:30 a.m.

(b) 11:45 p.m.

(c) 3:52 p.m.

Solution

(a) 0730

(b) Add 12 to the hours to give 2345.

(c) Add 12 to the hours to give 1552.

Example 2

Convert the following times from 24-hour clock to 'a.m.' or 'p.m.' times:

(a) 1426   (b) 0352   (c) 1833

Solution

(a) Subtract 12 from the hours to give 2:26 p.m.

(b) 3:52 a.m.

(c) Subtract 12 from the hours to give 6:33 p.m.

Note that a colon (:) is used to separate the hours from the minutes when using the 12-hour clock, whereas 24-hour clock times are written without a colon.

Example 3

Molly leaves Huddersfield at 1322 and arrives in London at 1805. How long does her journey take?

Solution   *Method A*

From 1322 to 1722 is 4 hours.

From 1722 to 1805 is 43 minutes.

Her journey takes 4 hours 43 minutes.

Method B

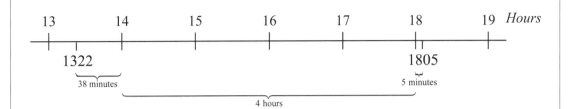

38 mins + 5 minutes = 43 minutes

Total time = 4 hours 43 minutes

Example 4

The time in the United Arab Emirates is 4 hours ahead of the time in the UK.

(a)   What is the time in the United Arab Emirates when it is 3:00 p.m. in the UK?

(b)   If it is 2:45 p.m. in the United Arab Emirates, what is the time in the UK?

Solution

(a)   The time in the United Arab Emirates is 4 hours ahead, so it is 7:00 p.m.

(b)   Four hours behind 2:45 p.m. is 10:45 a.m.

Exercises

1.   Convert the following times to 24-hour clock times:

   (a)   6:45 a.m.   (b)   6:45 p.m.   (c)   2:20 p.m.

   (d)   11:40 p.m.   (e)   10:30 a.m.   (f)   10:15 p.m.

2.   Write the following 24-hour clock times in 12-hour clock times, using 'a.m.' or 'p.m.':

   (a)   1642   (b)   0832   (c)   1042

   (d)   2236   (e)   2318   (f)   1520

3.   Which of the 24-hour clock times below are *not* possible times. Explain why.

   (a)   1372   (b)   1758

   (c)   2302   (d)   2536

4.   David gets on a train at 0845 and gets off at 1132. For how long is he on the train?

5.   A journey starts at 1532 and ends at 1830. How long does the journey take?

6.   Marco boards a ferry at 1842 and gets off at 0633 the next day. For how long is he on the ferry?

7.   In Venezuela the time is 4 hours behind the time in the UK.

     (a)   What is the time in Venezuela when it is 3:00 p.m. in the UK?

     (b)   What is the time in the UK when it is 2:30 p.m. in Venezuela?

     (c)   What is the time in the UK when it is 11:15 p.m. in Venezuela?

8.   The time in Norway is 1 hour ahead of the UK. It takes $3\frac{1}{2}$ hours to fly from the UK to Norway.

     (a)   A plane leaves the UK at 10:15 a.m. (UK time). What is the time in Norway when it lands there?

     (b)   The plane flies back and lands in the UK at 7:22 p.m. (UK time). At what time did the plane leave Norway?

9.   The time in Paraguay is 4 hours behind the UK.

     The time in Macao is 8 hours ahead of the UK.

     (a)   What is the time in Macao when it is 6:00 a.m. in Paraguay?

     (b)   What is the time in Paraguay when it is 3:30 p.m. in Macao?

     (c)   What is the time in Macao when it is 8:30 p.m. in Paraguay?

10. A ferry takes $26\frac{1}{2}$ hours to travel from the UK to Spain. The time in Spain is 1 hour ahead of the UK.

     When do you arrive in Spain if you leave the UK at:

     (a)   0830 on Monday   (b)   1742 on Friday   (c)   2342 on Sunday?

13.3 Time and Money

In this section we consider problems that involve both *time* and *money.*

Example 1

One day, Zoe works from 0930 until 1800.

She is paid £5.20 per hour.

How much does she earn for her day's work?

Solution

From 0930 until 1800 is $8\frac{1}{2}$ hours, so Zoe earns £5.20 × 8.5.

Now,
```
        5 2 0
    ×     8 5
    ─────────
      2 6 0 0
    4 1 6 0 0
    ─────────
    4 4 2 0 0
    ─────────
```

So 5.20 × 8.5 = 44.200, and Zoe earns £44.20.

Example 2

Robert works 40 hours each week and is paid £5.10 per hour.

He is given a 5% pay rise.

How much more does he earn per week after his pay rise?

Solution

Each week, Robert earns

$$40 \times £5.10 = £204.00$$

```
        5 1 0
    ×      4 0
    ─────────
    2 0 4 0 0
```

His increase each week

$$5\% \text{ of } £204 = \frac{5}{100} \times £204$$

$$= £10.20$$

Example 3

Esther is paid £4.50 per hour. She can work for up to 30 hours per week.

(a)   What is the maximum amount of money she can earn in a week?

(b)   How many hours should she work if she wants to earn £90 ?

Solution

(a)   The most she can earn in one week is

$$30 \times £4.50 = £135$$

```
        4 5 0
    ×      3 0
    ─────────
    1 3 5 0 0
```

31

(b)   £90 ÷ 4.50 = 900 ÷ 45   0 2 0

                     = 20 hours   45 | 9 0 0

Exercises

1.   The following table shows the times that people in a factory work on one day, and the rate they are paid per hour.

	Start Work	Finish Work	Hourly Rate
Janice	0830	1530	£3.80
Martin	0745	1415	£5.00
Gail	0950	1720	£4.20

How much does each person earn on this day?

2.   Des can choose between two jobs:

   Job A pays £3.80 per hour for 40 hours per week,

   Job B pays £4.50 per hour for 32 hours per week.

For which job will Des earn the most money per week?

3.   Heidi works as a cleaner at a hotel. She is paid £4.20 per hour. One day she starts work at 0645 and finishes at 1045. How much does she earn on that day?

4.   Briony earns £5 per hour working 12 hours per week in an evening job.

   (a)   How much does she earn per week?

   (b)   If she is given a 6% pay rise, how much does she now earn each week?

5.   Bill works the following hours in one week:

Monday	0745	to	1300
Tuesday	1400	to	2315
Wednesday	0630	to	1245
Thursday	0745	to	1430
Friday	1300	to	2330

He is paid £6.50 per hour.

   (a)   How many hours does he work during the week?

   (b)   How much does he earn for the week's work?

6. Kelly works from 0850 until 1400 on 6 days each week. She earns £4.30 per hour.

   (a) How many hours does she work per week?

   (b) How much does she earn per week?

   Kelly is given a 10% pay rise.

   (c) How much does she now earn per week?

7. In a year, Tony works 20 hours per week for 46 weeks and is paid a total of £5520.

   (a) How many hours does he work per year?

   (b) How much is he paid per hour?

   (c) If his wages are increased by 2%, how much will he now earn per year?

8. Sara works 30 hours per week, for which she is paid £135.

   (a) How much is she paid per hour?

   Her earnings increase to £140.40 per week.

   (b) How much is she now paid per hour?

   (c) Calculate the percentage increase in her earnings.

9. Ali is paid £14.70 for working from 0845 until 1215.

   (a) How much is he paid per hour?

   (b) How much would he be paid for working from 0840 until 1300 ?

   (c) What would be his hourly rate of pay, if it was increased by 3% ? Give your answer to the nearest pence.

10. Karen is paid £3.50 per hour for the first 40 hours she works in a week. She is paid an extra 25% per hour for any additional hours she works.

    How much does she earn for the week if she works the hours listed below:

Monday	0855	to	1650
Tuesday	0840	to	1710
Wednesday	0915	to	1805
Thursday	0855	to	1905
Friday	0900	to	1835

    Give your answer to the nearest pence.

14 Straight Line Graphs

14.1 Coordinates

You will have used coordinates in Unit 3 of Book Y7A. In this section, we revisit *coordinates* before starting work on *lines* and *graphs*.

Remember that the first number is the *x*-coordinate and the second number is the *y*-coordinate.

Example 1

What are the coordinates of the points marked on the following grid:

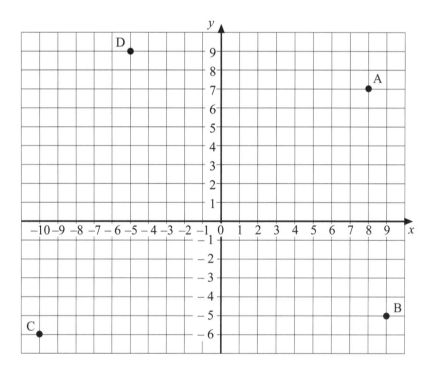

Solution

The coordinates are:

      A   (8, 7)

      B   (9, − 5)

      C   (− 10, − 6)

      D   (− 5, 9)

Example 2

The coordinates of the corners of a shape are (2, 4), (4, 1), (2, − 2), (− 2, − 2), (− 4, 1) and (− 2, 4).

(a)   Draw the shape.

(b)   What is the name of the shape?

Solution

(a)

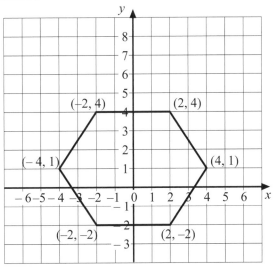

(b)   The shape has six sides and is called a *hexagon*.

Exercises

1.   Write down the coordinates of each of the points marked on the following axes:

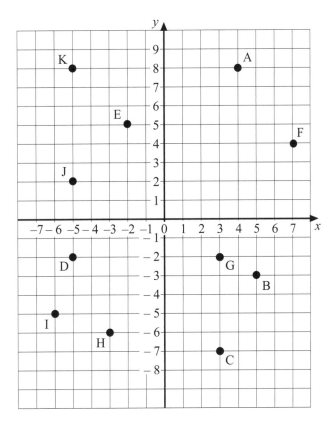

2. (a) Plot the points with coordinates $(3, -2)$, $(-1, 6)$ and $(-5, -2)$.

    (b) Join the points to form a triangle.

    (c) What type of triangle have you drawn?

3. (a) Plot the points with coordinates $(-1, 4)$, $(2, 5)$, $(5, 4)$ and $(2, -1)$.

    (b) Join these points, in order, to form a shape.

    (c) What is the name of the shape that you have drawn?

4. The coordinates of 3 corners of a square are $(3, 1)$, $(-1, 1)$ and $(3, -3)$. What are the coordinates of the other corner?

5. The coordinates of 3 corners of a rectangle are $(-1, 6)$, $(-4, 6)$ and $(-4, -5)$. What are the coordinates of the other corner?

6. A shape has corners at the points with coordinates $(3, -2)$, $(6, 2)$, $(-2, 2)$ and $(-5, -2)$.

    (a) Draw the shape.

    (b) What is the name of the shape?

7. A shape has corners at the points with coordinates $(3, 1)$, $(1, -3)$, $(3, -7)$ and $(5, -3)$.

    (a) Draw the shape.

    (b) What is the name of the shape?

8. (a) Join the points with the coordinates below, in order, to form a polygon:

         $(-5, 0)$, $(-3, 2)$, $(-1, 2)$, $(1, 0)$, $(1, -2)$, $(-1, -4)$, $(-3, -4)$ and $(-5, -2)$.

    (b) What is the name of the polygon?

9. Three of the corners of a parallelogram have coordinates $(1, 5)$, $(4, 4)$ and $(6, -3)$.

    (a) Draw the parallelogram.

    (b) What are the coordinates of the other corner?

10. Ben draws a pattern by joining, in order, the points with the following coordinates:

    $(-2, 1)$, $(-2, 2)$ $(0, 2)$, $(0, -1)$, $(-4, -1)$, $(-4, 4)$, $(2, 4)$ and $(2, -3)$.

    What are the coordinates of the next three points he would use?

14.2 Plotting Points on Straight Lines

In this section we plot points that lie on a straight line, and look for relationships between the coordinates of these points.

Example 1

(a)   Plot the points with coordinates:

$(1, 2)$, $(2, 3)$, $(3, 4)$, $(4, 5)$ and $(5, 6)$.

(b)   Draw a straight line through these points.

(c)   Describe how the x- and y-coordinates of these points are related.

Solution

(a)   The points are plotted below:

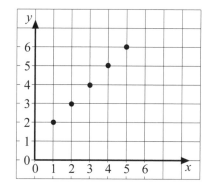

(b)   A straight line can be drawn through these points:

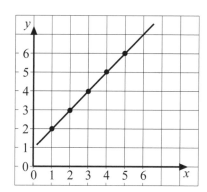

(c)   The y-coordinate is always one more than the x-coordinate, so we can write
       $y = x + 1$.

Example 2

(a)   Plot the points with coordinates:

(0, 0), (1, 3), (3, 9) and (5, 15).

(b)   Draw a straight line through these points

(c)   Write down the coordinates of two other points on this line.

(d)   Describe how the *x*- and *y*-coordinates are related.

Solution

(a)   The points are plotted below:

(b)   A line can then be drawn through these points:

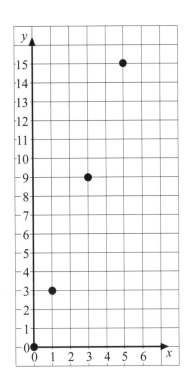

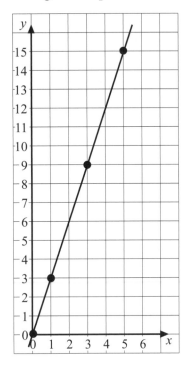

(c)   The points (2, 6), and (4, 12) also lie on the line (and many others).

(d)   The *y*-coordinate is 3 times the *x*-coordinate. So we can write $y = 3x$

Exercises

1. (a) Plot the points with coordinates
$$(0, 4), \ (1, 5), \ (3, 7) \text{ and } (5, 9).$$

   (b) Draw a straight line through the points.

   (c) Write down the coordinates of 3 other points that lie on this line.

2. (a) Plot the points with coordinates
$$(0, 6), \ (2, 4), \ (3, 3) \text{ and } (5, 1)$$
   and draw a straight line through them.

   (b) On the same graph as used for question 2 (a), plot the points with coordinates
$$(1, 8), \ (2, 7), \ (5, 4) \text{ and } (7, 2)$$
   and draw a straight line through them.

   (c) Copy and complete the sentence:

   "These two lines are p..................... ".

3. (a) Plot the points with coordinates
$$(2, 6), \ (3, 5), \ (4, 4) \text{ and } (7, 1)$$
   and draw a straight line through them.

   (b) On the same set of axes, plot the points with coordinates
$$(0, 1), \ (1, 2), \ (3, 4) \text{ and } (5, 6)$$
   and draw a straight line through them.

   (c) Copy and complete this sentence:

   "These two lines are p..................... ".

4. (a) Plot the points with coordinates
$$(1, 1), \ (2, 2), \ (4, 4) \text{ and } (5, 5)$$
   and draw a straight line through them.

   (b) Write down the coordinates of two other points on the line.

   (c) Describe the relationship between the x- and y-coordinates.

5. The points $(1, 3), \ (2, 4), \ (3, 5)$ and $(5, 7)$ lie on a straight line.

   (a) Plot these points and draw the line.

   (b) Write down the coordinates of 3 other points on the line.

   (c) Describe the relationship between the x- and y-coordinates.

6. (a) Plot the points (0, 5), (2, 3), (4, 1) and (5, 0). Draw a straight line through them.

   (b) Write down the coordinates of two other points on the line.

   (c) The relationship between the x- and y-coordinates can be written as

   $x + y = \boxed{}$. What is the missing number?

7. (a) Plot the points with coordinates

   $(-3, -4)$, $(-1, -2)$, $(1, 0)$, $(4, 3)$

   (b) Draw a straight line graph through these points.

   (c) Describe the relationship between the x- and y-coordinates.

8. The points with coordinates $(-2, -4)$, $(2, 4)$, $(3, 6)$ and $(4, 8)$ lie on a straight line.

   (a) Draw the line.

   (b) Describe the relationship between the x- and y-coordinates of points on the line.

9. The points with coordinates $(-6, -3)$, $(-1, 2)$, $(2, 5)$ and $(4, 7)$ lie on a straight line.

   (a) Draw the line.

   (b) Complete the missing numbers in the coordinates of other points that lie on the line:

   $(-7, \boxed{})$, $(\boxed{}, -1)$, $(3, \boxed{})$, $(\boxed{}, 4)$, $(100, \boxed{})$

   (c) Describe the relationship between the x- and y-coordinates of the points on the line.

   (d) Will the point with coordinates $(25, 27)$ lie on the line? Give a reason for your answer.

10. Each set of points listed below lies on a straight line. Plot the points, draw the line, and complete the statement about the relationship between the x- and y-coordinates.

    (a) $(1, 6)$, $(3, 4)$, $(8, -1)$ $x + y = \boxed{}$

    (b) $(-4, 2)$, $(-1, 5)$, $(3, 9)$ $y = x + \boxed{}$

    (c) $(-2, -8)$, $(0, 0)$, $(3, 12)$ $y = \boxed{} x$

    (d) $(-4, -6)$, $(-1, -3)$, $(3, 1)$ $y = x - \boxed{}$

14.3 Plotting Graphs Given Their Equations

In this section we see how to plot a graph, given its equation. We also look at how steep it is and use the word *gradient* to describe this. There is a simple connection between the equation of a line and its gradient, which you will notice as you work through this section.

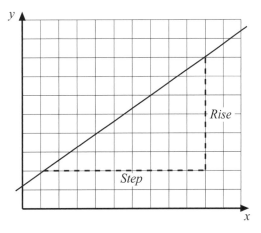

Gradient of a Line

$$Gradient = \frac{Rise}{Step}$$

You can draw any triangle using the sides to determine the rise and step, but the triangle must have *one side horizontal* and *one side vertical*.

Example 1

Determine the gradient of each of the following lines:

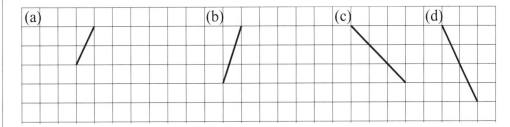

(a)   (b)   (c)   (d)

Solution

(a)

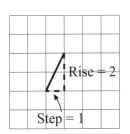

Rise = 2

Step = 1

$$Gradient = \frac{Rise}{Step}$$

$$= \frac{2}{1}$$

$$= 2$$

(b)

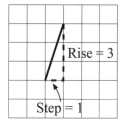

Gradient $= \dfrac{\text{Rise}}{\text{Step}}$

$= \dfrac{3}{1}$

$= 3$

(c)

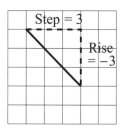

Gradient $= \dfrac{\text{Rise}}{\text{Step}}$

$= \dfrac{(-3)}{3}$

$= -1$

Note that in (c) the rise is *negative* although the step is *positive*, so the gradient of the line is *negative*.

(d)

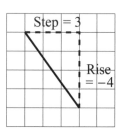

Gradient $= \dfrac{\text{Rise}}{\text{Step}}$

$= \dfrac{(-4)}{3}$

$= -\dfrac{4}{3}$

Note that in (d) once again the rise is *negative,* and the step is *positive*, so the gradient of the line is *negative*.

(In both (c) and (d) you will see that the lines slope in a different direction to the lines in (a) and (b), which have a positive gradient.)

Example 2

(a)   Complete the table below for $y = 2x + 1$.

x	-2	-1	0	1	2
y					

(b)   Use the information in the table to plot the graph with equation $y = 2x + 1$.

Solution

(a)

x	-2	-1	0	1	2
y	-3	-1	1	3	5

(b) The points

(−2, −3), (−1, −1), (0, 1)

(1, 3) and (2, 5)

can then be plotted, and a
straight line drawn through
these points.

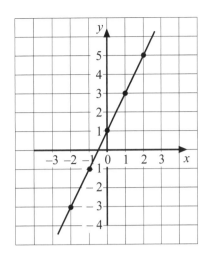

Example 3

(a) Draw the graph of the line with equation $y = x + 1$.

(b) What is the gradient of the line?

Solution

(a) The table shows how to calculate the coordinates of some points on the line.

x	− 3	− 2	− 1	0	1	2	3
y	− 2	− 1	0	1	2	3	4

The points with coordinates $(-3, -2)$, $(-2, -1)$, $(-1, 0)$, $(0, 1)$, $(1, 2)$, $(2, 3)$ and $(3, 4)$ can then be plotted and a line drawn as shown:

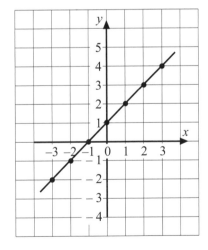

(b) To calculate the gradient of the line, draw a triangle under the line as shown in the diagram on the next page. The triangle can be of any size, but must have one horizontal side and one vertical side.

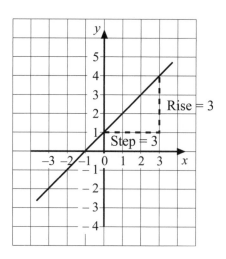

$$\text{Gradient} \ = \ \frac{\text{Rise}}{\text{Step}}$$

$$= \ \frac{3}{3}$$

$$= \ 1$$

Exercises

1. Which of the following lines have a *positive* gradient and which have a *negative* gradient:

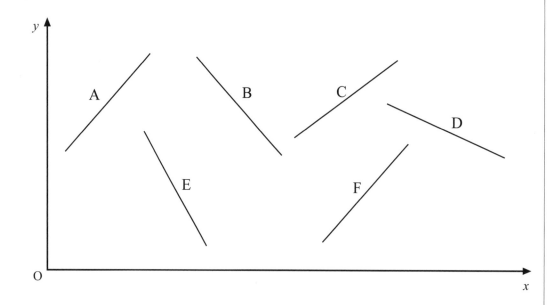

2.   Determine the gradient of each of the following lines:

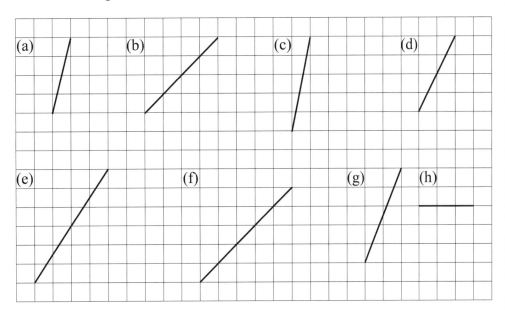

3.   Determine the gradient of each of the following lines:

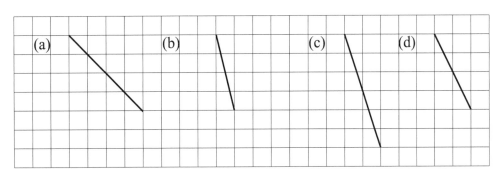

4.   (a)   Copy and complete the following table for $y = x - 2$.

x	-3	-2	-1	0	1	2	3
y				-2			

     (b)   Draw the line with equation $y = x - 2$.

5.   (a)   Copy and complete the following table for $y = 2x + 3$.

x	-3	-2	-1	0	1	2	3
y							9

     (b)   Draw the line with equation $y = 2x + 3$.

6. (a) Draw the line with equation $y = 2x - 1$.

    (b) Determine the gradient of this line.

7. (a) Draw the line with equation $y = \dfrac{1}{2}x + 2$.

    (b) Determine the gradient of this line.

8. (a) Draw the lines $y = 3x + 1$ and $y = 4x - 5$.

    (b) Determine the gradient of each of these lines.

9. Without drawing the lines, state the gradients of the lines with the following equations:

    (a) $y = 2x + 4$

    (b) $y = 3x - 9$

    (c) $y = 10x + 1$

    (d) $y = 5x + 3$

10. (a) Draw the lines and equations $y = 2x + 1$ and $y = 3x - 2$.

    (b) Write down the coordinates of the point where these two lines cross.

11. Determine the coordinates of the point where the lines $y = x + 3$ and $y = 7 - x$ cross.

12. (a) Draw the line with equation $y = 6 - 2x$.

    (b) Explain why the gradient of this line is -2.

13. (a) Explain why the lines with equations $y = 2 - 2x$ and $y = 5 - 2x$ are parallel.

    (b) Write down the equation of another line that would be parallel to these lines.

    (c) Draw all three lines.

14.4 The Equation of a Straight Line

In this section we examine how the equation of a straight line contains information about the gradient of the line and the point where it crosses the y-axis.

The intercept is c, that is the point where the line crosses the y-axis.

The gradient is m, where

$$m = \frac{\text{Rise}}{\text{Step}}$$

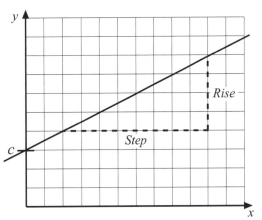

The equation of a straight line is $y = mx + c$.

Example 1

(a) Determine the equation of the line shown below:

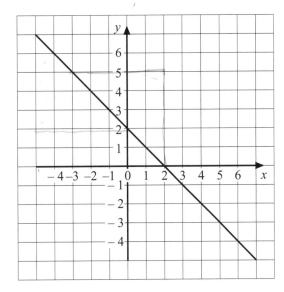

Solution

First note that the intercept is 2, so we write $c = 2$.

Next calculate the gradient of the line.

Note that the rise is -6, as the line is going down as you move from left to right.

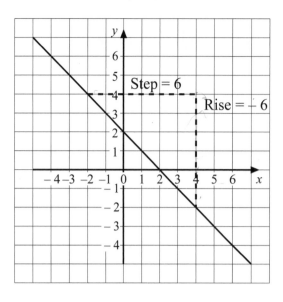

Gradient $= \dfrac{-6}{6}$

$= -1.$

So $\quad m = -1$

The equation of a straight line is $y = mx + c$, so here, with $m = -1$ and $c = 2$, we have

$$y = -x + 2$$

or

$$y = 2 - x.$$

Reminder

Recall that $-1 \times x = -1x$ is written as $-x$ for speed and convenience.

 Exercises

1.   (a)   Draw the line with equation $y = 2x + 3$.

      (b)   Determine the gradient of this line.

      (c)   What is the intercept of this line?

2.   (a)   Draw the lines with equations $y = x$, $y = -x$, $y = 2x$ and $y = -3x$.

      (b)   Determine the gradient of each of these lines.

      (c)   What is the intercept of each of these lines?

3.   The points with coordinates $(-2, 3)$, $(0, 5)$ and $(3, 8)$ lie on a straight line.

      (a)   Plot the points and draw the line.

      (b)   Determine the gradient of the line.

      (c)   What is the intercept of the line?

      (d)   Write down the equation of the line.

4.   Determine the equation of each of the lines shown below:

(a)

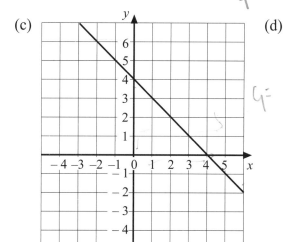

$\frac{31}{3} =$

$y = x - \overset{3}{3}$

(b)

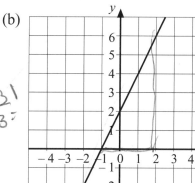

$\frac{6}{3} =$

$G = 2$

$y = 2x + 2$

(c)

$G =$

$y = -x + 4$

(d)

$\frac{6}{2} = 3$

$y = -3x + 2$

5.   Copy and complete the following table:

Equation	Gradient	Intercept
$y = 2x + 7$		
	8	-2
$y = 8 - 3x$		
	7	-5
	-3	2
	-5	-2

49

6. (a) Draw the lines with equations $y = x + 1$, $y = 1 - x$, $y = 2x + 1$ and
        $y = 3x + 1$ on the same set of axes.

    (b) Explain why these lines all pass through the same point on the y-axis.

7. The points with coordinates $(-2, -6)$, $(0, 0)$ and $(3, 9)$ all lie on a straight
    line.

    (a) What is the gradient of the line?

    (b) What is the intercept of the line?

    (c) What is the equation of the line?

    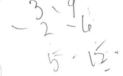

8. Draw lines which have:

    (a) gradient 2 and intercept 3,

    (b) gradient $\dfrac{1}{2}$ and intercept 1,

    (c) gradient -4 and intercept 7.

14.5 The Equation of a Line Given Two Points

If you know the coordinates of two points on a line, it is possible to determine its
equation *without drawing the line*.

> If a line passes through the points with coordinates (x_1, y_1) and (x_2, y_2),
> the gradient, m, of the line is given by
>
> $$m = \frac{y_2 - y_1}{x_2 - x_1}$$

Example 1

Determine the equation of the line that joins the points with coordinates $(4, 8)$ and
$(10, 11)$.

Solution

First determine the gradient of the line:

$$m = \frac{11 - 8}{10 - 4}$$

$$= \frac{3}{6}$$

$$= \frac{1}{2}$$

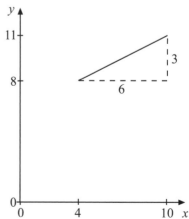

Now the equation must be $y = \dfrac{1}{2}x + c$.

To determine c, use the values of x and y from one of the points. Here $x = 4$ and $y = 8$, and substitute in the equation, giving:

$$8 = \frac{1}{2} \times 4 + c$$

$$8 = 2 + c$$

$$c = 6$$

So the equation of the line is given by $y = \dfrac{1}{2}x + 6$.

Exercises

1. A straight line joins the points with coordinates $(1, 1)$ and $(4, 7)$.

   (a) Determine the gradient of the line.

   (b) Determine the equation of the line.

2. Determine the equation of the line that passes through the points $(0, 0)$ and $(3, 21)$.

3. Explain why a line that passes through the point $(0, 0)$ and any other point has equation $y = mx$.

4. Determine the equation of a straight line that passes through the following pairs of points:

   (a) $(0, 1)$ and $(5, 16)$ (b) $(3, 20)$ and $(7, 32)$

   (c) $(0, 100)$ and $(50, 0)$ (d) $(-1, 9)$ and $(3, -3)$

   (e) $(-6, -4)$ and $(10, 28)$ (f) $(-6, -2)$ and $(-2, -9)$

5. A line has gradient -4 and passes through the point with coordinates $(5, 7)$. What is the equation of the line?

6. A triangle has corners at the points with coordinates $(1, 2)$, $(-2, 3)$ and $(0, -1)$. Determine the equations of the lines that form the sides of the triangle.

7. A parallelogram has corners at the points with coordinates $(-1, 1)$, $(0, 3)$, $(2, -1)$ and $(1, -3)$. Determine the equations of the lines that form the sides of the parallelogram.

15 Polygons

15.1 Angle Facts

In this section we revise some basic work with *angles*, and begin by using the three rules listed below:

The angles at a point add up to 360 °, e.g.

$$a + b + c = 360°$$

The angles on a straight line add up to 180 °, e.g.

$$e + f = 180°$$

The angles in a triangle add up to 180 °, e.g.

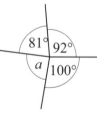

$$w + x + y = 180°$$

Example 1

Determine the size of angle a in the diagram shown.

Solution

$$81° + 92° + 100° + a = 360° \text{ (angle sum at a point)}$$
$$a + 273° = 360°$$
$$a = 87°$$

Example 2

Determine the size of angle d in the diagram shown.

Solution

$$105° + 42° + d = 180° \text{ (angle sum in a triangle)}$$
$$147° + d = 180°$$
$$d = 33°$$

Example 3

Determine the size of angle n in the diagram shown.

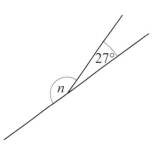

Solution

$n + 27° = 180°$ *(angle sum on a line)*

$n = 153°$

Exercises

1. Calculate the sizes of the angles marked by letters in the following diagrams:

(a)

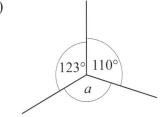

(b)

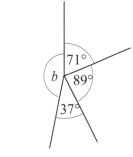

(c)

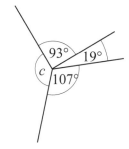

(d)

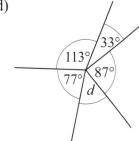

2. Calculate the sizes of the unknown angles in the following triangles:

(a)

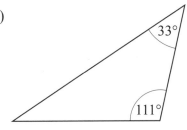

(b)

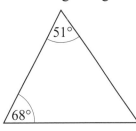

(c)

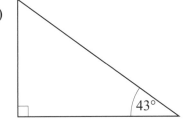

(d)

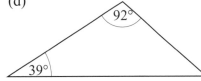

3. Calculate the sizes of the angles marked by the letter *x* in the following
    diagrams:

    (a)
    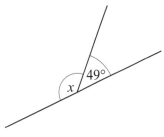

    (b)
    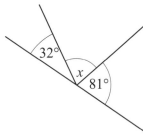

    (c)
    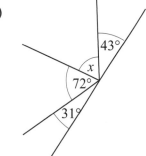

    (d)
    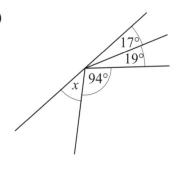

4. The diagram shows an isosceles triangle.
    What are the sizes of the two angles marked *a* and *b* ?

    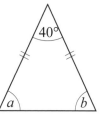

5. Calculate the sizes of the angles
    marked *a* and *b* in the diagram.

    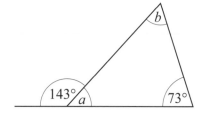

6. The diagram opposite shows two intersecting
    straight lines. Calculate the sizes of the
    angles marked *a*, *b* and *c* in the diagram.

    What do you notice about
    angles *a* and *c* ?

    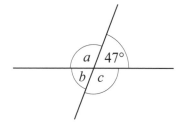

7. The diagram opposite shows a rectangle
    and its diagonals. Calculate the sizes of
    the angles marked *a*, *b* and *c*.

    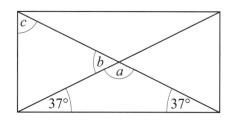

8.   Determine the sizes of the angles
     marked *a*, *b* and *c* in the diagram
     shown.

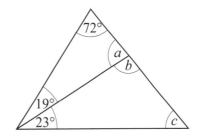

9.   PQR is a straight line. Determine the
     sizes of the angles marked *a*, *b* and *c*
     in the triangles shown.

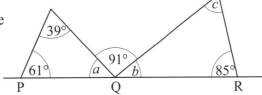

10. Calculate the sizes of the angles marked
     a, *b*, *c*, *d* and *e* in the triangles shown.

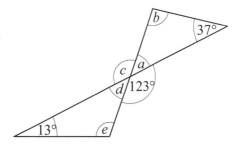

15.2 Angle Properties of Polygons

In this section we calculate the size of the *interior* and *exterior* angles for different regular polygons.

The following diagram shows a regular hexagon:

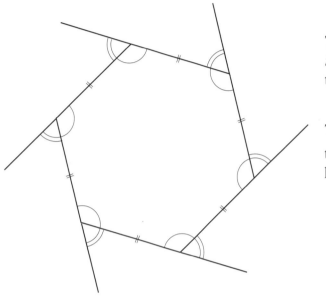

The angles marked are the *interior* angles of the hexagon.

The angles marked are the *exterior* angles of the hexagon.

In a regular polygon the sides are all the same length and the *interior* angles are all the same size.

> Note that, for any polygon:
>
> interior angle + exterior angle = $180°$.

Since the interior angles of a regular polygon are all the same size, it follows that the exterior angles are also equal to one another.

One complete turn of the hexagon above will rotate any one exterior angle to each of the others in turn, which illustrates the following result:

> The exterior angles of *any* polygon add up to $360°$.

 ## Example 1

Calculate the sizes of the *interior* and the *exterior* angles of a regular hexagon. Hence determine the sum of the interior angles.

 ### Solution

The exterior angles of a regular hexagon are all equal, as shown in the previous diagram.

Therefore the exterior angle of a regular hexagon $= \dfrac{360°}{6}$

$$= 60°$$

So the interior angle of a regular hexagon $\quad = \quad 180° - 60°$

$$= \quad 120°$$

The sum of the interior angles $\quad = \quad 6 \times 120°$

$$= \quad 720°$$

Example 2

The *exterior* angle of a regular polygon is $40°$.

Calculate:

(a)   the size of the *interior* angle,

(b)   the number of sides of the polygon.

Solution

(a)   Interior angle + exterior angle $= 180°$

Interior angle $= 180° - 40°$

$$= 140°$$

(b)   The number of sides can be determined by dividing $360°$ by the size of the exterior angles, giving

$$\dfrac{360}{40} = 9$$

so the polygon has 9 sides.

In a regular polygon:

exterior angle	$=$	$\dfrac{360°}{\text{the number of sides}}$
number of sides	$=$	$\dfrac{360°}{\text{exterior angle}}$

Exercises

1.   Calculate the size of the *exterior* angles of a regular polygon which has interior angles of:

   — (a)   150 ° 30

   ✓ (b)   175 °

   — (c)   162 ° 18

   ✓ (d)   174 °

2.   Calculate the sizes of the *exterior* and *interior* angles of: $\frac{360}{8} = 45$ Ex $180 - 45 = 135$

   ✗ (a)   a regular octagon,

   ✓ (b)   a regular decagon.

3.   (a)   Calculate the size of the *interior* angles of a regular 12-sided polygon.

   ✓ (b)   What is the sum of the *interior* angles of a regular 12-sided polygon?
            $\frac{360}{12} = 30 = 15$

4.   (a)   What is the size of the *interior* angle of a regular 20-sided polygon?

   (b)   What is the sum of the *interior* angles of a regular 20-sided polygon?

5.   Calculate the size of the *exterior* angle of a regular pentagon.

6.   The size of the exterior angle of a regular polygon is 12 °. How many sides does this polygon have?

7.   Calculate the number of sides of a regular polygon with interior angles of:

   (a)   (i)   150 °   (ii)   175 °

          (iii)   162 °   (iv)   174 °

   (b)   Show why it is impossible for a regular polygon to have an interior angle of 123 °.

8.   (a)   Complete the following table for regular polygons. Note that many of the missing values can be found in the examples and earlier exercises for this unit.

Number of Sides	Exterior Angles	Interior Angles	Sum of Interior Angles
4	90 °		
5			
6			
7			
8			
9			
10			
12			

(b) Describe an alternative way to calculate the sum of the interior angles of a regular polygon.

(c) Draw and measure the angles in some irregular polygons. Which of the results in the table are also true for irregular polygons?

9. The exterior angle of a regular polygon is 4 °.

ext *int* $\frac{360}{4} = 90$
176.

(a) How many sides does the polygon have? 90

(b) What is the sum of the interior angles of the polygon? $176 \times 90 = 15840$

10. A regular polygon has n sides.

(a) Explain why the exterior angles of the polygon are of size $\frac{360°}{n}$. $= \frac{360}{no. \ of \ sides}$

(b) Explain why the interior angles of the polygon are $180° - \frac{360°}{n}$.

(c) Write an expression for the sum of the interior angles.

15.3 Symmetry

In this section we revise the *symmetry* of objects and examine the symmetry of regular polygons.

Example 1

Draw the lines of symmetry of each shape below:

(a)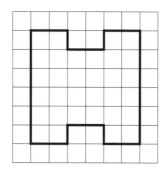

(b)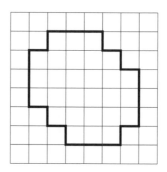

Solution

(a) The shape has 2 lines of symmetry, one horizontal and the other vertical, as shown below:

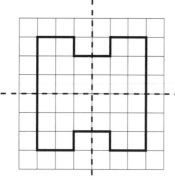

(b) The shape has 2 diagonal lines of symmetry, as shown below:

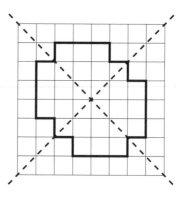

> *Reminder*
>
> The order of rotational symmetry is the number of times in one rotation of 360 ° that a shape is identical to that of its starting position.

Example 2

What is the order of rotational symmetry of each of the following shapes:

(a)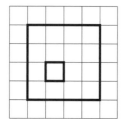

(b)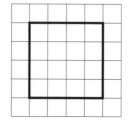

(c)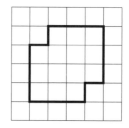

Solution

(a) The shape has rotational symmetry of order 1, meaning that it does not have rotational symmetry. (The shape cannot be rotated to another position within 360 ° and still look the same.)

(b) The shape has rotational symmetry of order 4.

The following diagram shows how the position of one corner, marked *, moves as the square is rotated anticlockwise about its centre.

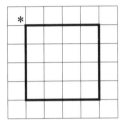
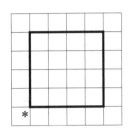
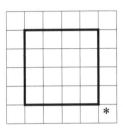
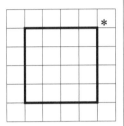

(c) The shape has rotational symmetry of order 2. The diagram shows the position of a corner, marked *, as the shape is rotated about its centre.

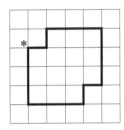
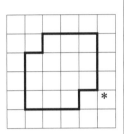

Example 3

A heptagon is a shape which has 7 sides.

(a) Draw a diagram to show the lines of symmetry of a regular heptagon.

(b) What is the order of rotational symmetry of a regular heptagon?

Solution

(a) A regular heptagon has 7 lines of symmetry, as shown in the following diagram:

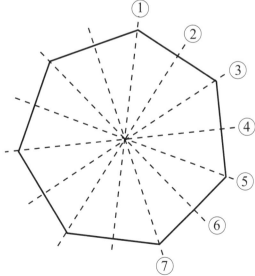

(b)   A regular heptagon has rotational symmetry of order 7.

> The order of rotational symmetry and the number of lines of symmetry of *any regular* polygon is equal to the number of sides.

Exercises

1.   Copy each of the following shapes and draw in all the lines of symmetry. For each one, state the order of rotational symmetry and mark on your copy its centre of rotation.

(a)
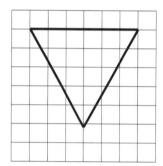

(b)
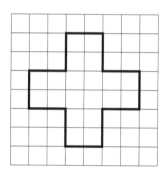

(c)
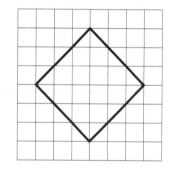

(d)
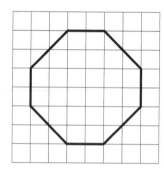

(e)
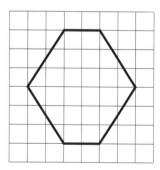

(f)
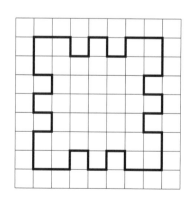

2. State the order of rotational symmetry and the number of lines of symmetry, for each of the following shapes:

(a)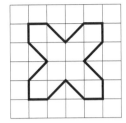

(b)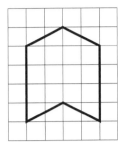

(c)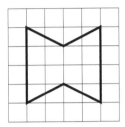

(d)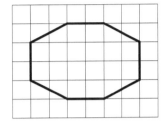

(e)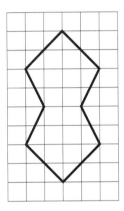

(f)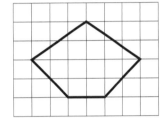

3. Describe fully the symmetries of the following shapes:

(a)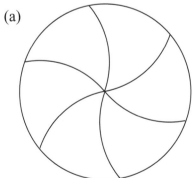

(b)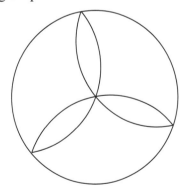

4. Describe the symmetry properties of each of the following triangles:

  Equilateral   *Isosceles*   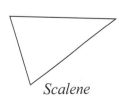 *Scalene*

5.   (a)   How many lines of symmetry does a *square* have?
          Draw a diagram to show this information.

     (b)   What is the order of rotational symmetry of a *square*?

6.   (a)   Copy and complete the following table:

Shape	Order of Rotational Symmetry	Number of Lines of Symmetry
Equilateral triangle		
Square		
Regular pentagon		
Regular hexagon		
Regular heptagon (7 sides)		
Regular octagon		
Regular nonagon (9 sides)		
Regular decagon (10 sides)		
Regular dodecagon (12 sides)		

     (b)   What do you conclude from the information in the table?

7.   Draw a shape that has *no* lines of symmetry, but has rotational symmetry of order 3.

8.   Draw a shape that has *at least one* line of symmetry and *no* rotational symmetry.

9.   Draw two regular polygons, one with an *even* number of sides and one with an *odd* number of sides. By drawing lines of symmetry on each diagram, show how the positions of the lines of symmetry differ between *odd-* and *even-sided* regular polygons.

10. Draw an irregular polygon that has both *line* and *rotational* symmetry. Show the lines of symmetry and the centre of rotation, and state its order of rotational symmetry.

15.4 Quadrilaterals

There are many special types of quadrilaterals; the following table lists some of them and their properties.

Quadrilateral	Properties	
Rectangle	4 right angles and opposite sides equal	
Square	4 right angles and 4 equal sides	
Parallelogram	Two pairs of parallel sides and opposite sides equal	
Rhombus	Parallelogram with 4 equal sides	
Trapezium	Two sides are parallel	
Kite	Two pairs of adjacent sides of the same length	

Example 1

List the quadrilaterals that have four sides all of the *same length*.

Solution

Square and *rhombus*.

Example 2

List the quadrilaterals that do *not* have two pairs of parallel sides.

Solution

Kite and *trapezium.*

Example 3

Which quadrilaterals have diagonals that are *perpendicular* to one another?

Solution

The *square, rhombus* and *kite* have diagonals that cross at right angles.

Exercises

1.   Which quadrilaterals have diagonals that are the same length?

2.   (a)   Which quadrilaterals have *exactly two* lines of symmetry?

     (b)   Draw diagrams to show these lines of symmetry.

3.   Which quadrilaterals have rotational symmetry of order 2 ?

4.   (a)   Which quadrilaterals can have *exactly one* line of symmetry?

     (b)   Draw diagrams to show them and the line of symmetry.

5.   Name each of the following quadrilaterals:

(a)

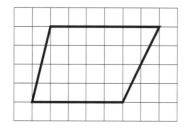

(b)

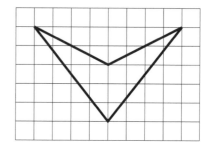

(c)

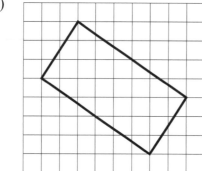

(d)

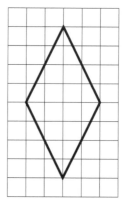

(e)

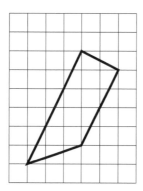

(f)

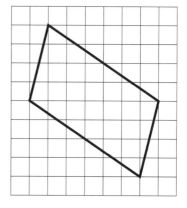

6. Which quadrilaterals have diagonals that are *not* equal in length?

7. A quadrilateral has four sides of the same length. Copy and complete the following sentences:

   (a) The quadrilateral must be a ....

   (b) The quadrilateral could be a .... if ....

8. (a) Which quadrilaterals have *more than one* line of symmetry?

   (b) Draw diagrams to show them and their lines of symmetry.

   (c) Which quadrilaterals have rotational symmetry of order *greater than 1* ? List these quadrilaterals and state the order of their rotational symmetry.

9. The following flow chart is used to identify quadrilaterals:

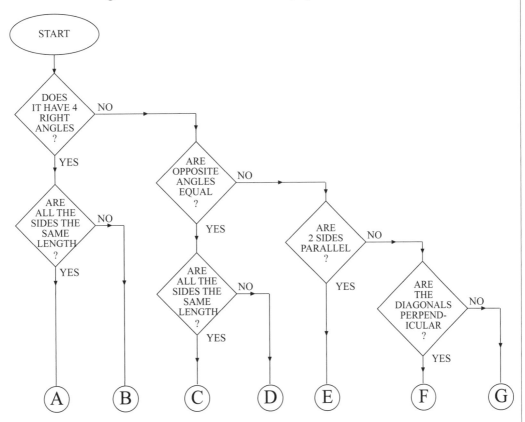

   Which type of quadrilateral arrives at each of the outputs, A to G ?

10. The following flow chart can be used to classify quadrilaterals, but some
     question boxes are empty. Copy and complete the flow chart.

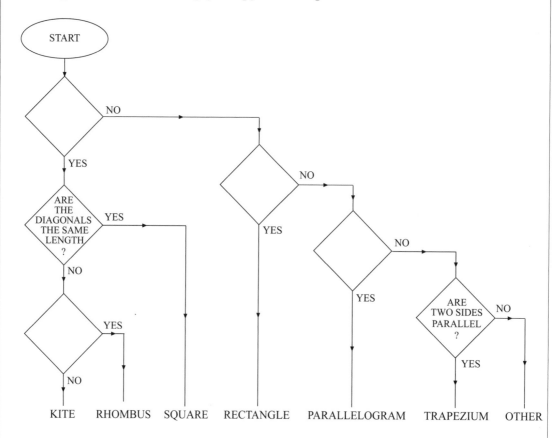

16 Circles and Cylinders

16.1 Introduction to Circles

In this section we consider the circle, looking at drawing circles and at the lines that split circles into different parts.

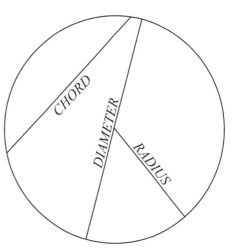

A *chord* joins any two points on the circumference of a circle.

A *diameter* is a chord that passes through the centre of the circle.

A *radius* joins the centre of the circle to any point on the circumference of the circle.

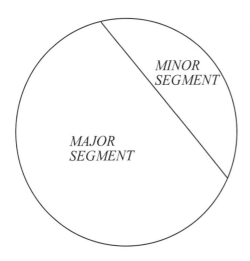

A chord splits a circle into two *segments*.

The larger one is called a *major segment*: the smaller one is the *minor segment*.

The part of a circle between two radii is called a *sector*.

The part of the circle that forms the curved side of the sector is called an *arc*.

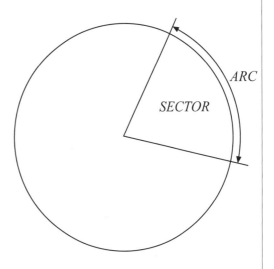

Example 1

(a)   Draw a circle of radius 5 cm.

(b)   Draw a radius of the circle.

(c)   Draw a chord that is perpendicular to the radius and is 3.3 cm from the centre of the circle.

(d)   Measure the length of the chord.

Solution

(a)   First draw the circle.

(b)   Then draw in a radius.

(c)   Measure 3.3 cm along the radius from the centre of the circle. Draw a chord at right angles to the radius and through this point.

(d)   Measure the chord, which gives 7.5 cm.

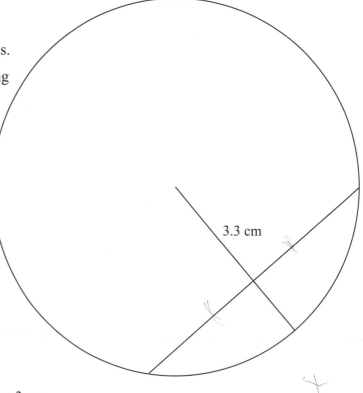

3.3 cm

Example 2

(a)   Draw a circle of radius 3 cm.

(b)   Draw a chord of length 5 cm, inside the circle.

(c)   Draw the perpendicular bisector of the chord.

(d)   What is the length of the new chord that is formed by the perpendicular bisector?

Solution

(a)   First draw the circle.

(b)   Put your compass point at A, with your compass set at 5 cm. Draw an arc to find the point B. Then join the points A and B.

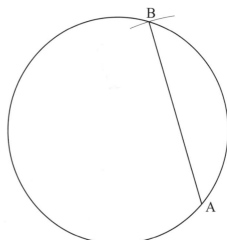

(c)   To draw a perpendicular bisector, place your compass point at A and draw
two arcs. Repeat with your compass point at B, drawing arcs of the same
radius as before, so that they intersect. Draw a line through the two
intersections.

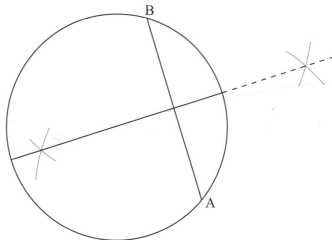

(d)   Measure the length of the new chord as 6 cm. The new chord is, in fact, a
diameter of the circle.

Exercises

1.   The diagram shows a circle with centre, O. What is the name given to each
of the following lines:

(a)   O A   (b)   A B   (c)   B C   (d)   O D

(e)   C D   (f)   A C   (g)   A D

OA = radius

AB

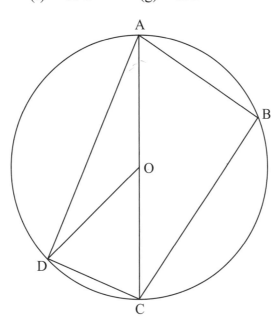

2. Which of the parts of the circle shown are:

    (a) sectors,

    (b) segments,

    (c) triangles?

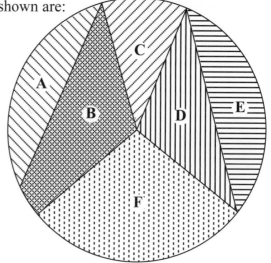

3. (a) Draw a circle of radius 5 cm.

    (b) Draw any chord in this circle.

    (c) Draw the perpendicular bisector of the chord.

    (d) Draw 2 other chords and their perpendicular bisectors.

    (e) Comment on the perpendicular bisectors of the chords.

4. (a) Draw a circle of radius 4 cm and a chord of length 3 cm, in the circle.

    (b) Join the ends of the chord to the centre of the circle, to form a triangle.

    (c) What length is the perimeter of the triangle?

5. The diagram shows a sketch of a triangle which is drawn inside a circle of radius 3 cm.

    (a) Draw this triangle accurately.

    (b) Determine the perimeter of the triangle.

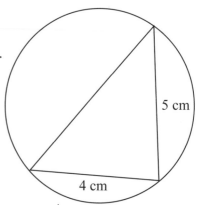

6. The diagram shows a triangle drawn inside a circle of radius 5 cm. The line A B is a diameter.

    (a) Draw this triangle accurately.

    (b) Determine the length of A C.

    (c) Determine the size of the angle A C B.

    (d) Calculate the area of the triangle.

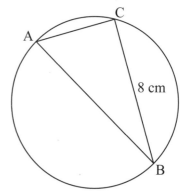

7. In a circle of radius 2.5 cm, draw a radius and the chord that is a perpendicular bisector to the radius. What is the length of this chord?

8. A triangle is drawn so that the 3 corners are on a circle of radius 3 cm. Two of the sides have length 5 cm.

 (a) Draw the triangle.

 (b) Determine the length of the third side.

 (c) Draw the perpendicular bisector of each side of the triangle.

 (d) How far is it along each perpendicular bisector from the side to the centre of the circle?

9. (a) Draw any triangle.

 (b) Draw the perpendicular bisector of each side.

 (c) Draw a circle with its centre at the point where the perpendicular bisectors intersect, and that passes through the three corners of the triangle.

10. Draw a circle of radius 3 cm. A chord in the circle has length 4 cm. Determine the distance from the centre of the chord to the centre of the circle.

16.2 Estimating the Circumference of a Circle

In this section we investigate the relationship between the *diameter* and the *circumference* of a circle. The circumference is the distance round the outside of a circle.

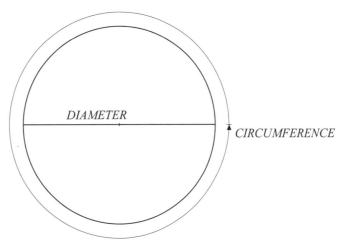

Example 1

Measure the diameter and circumference
of the circle shown.

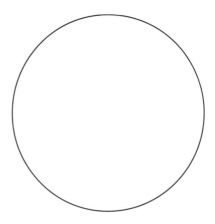

Solution

The diameter can be measured directly as 5.2 cm.

To measure the circumference, take a piece of
string and lay it round the outside of the circle.

Then lay the string along a ruler and
measure the circumference as 16.3 cm.

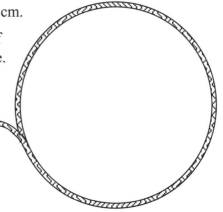

Reminder

The points shown below form a *scatter graph*.

The line drawn on the graph is called the 'line of best fit': it is the straight
line which best fits the points plotted. It does not have to go through
every point; just as close to them as possible. The line should be
positioned so that approximately the same number of points are above it
as below it.

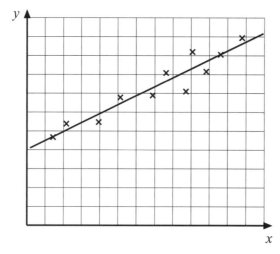

You will need to draw lines of best fit as you work through this unit.

Exercises

1. (a) Draw circles of radius 1 cm, 2 cm, 3 cm, 4 cm, 5 cm and 6 cm.

    (b) Measure the circumference and diameter of each circle.

2. (a) Obtain a number of circular objects, for example,

    > *bottle of squash,*
    >
    > *tin of baked beans,*
    >
    > *bottle of Tippex,*
    >
    > *roll of Sellotape,* etc.

    (b) For each object, measure the diameter and the circumference.

3. (a) Draw a scatter graph to show your results from questions 1 and 2, on a set of axes like those that follow:

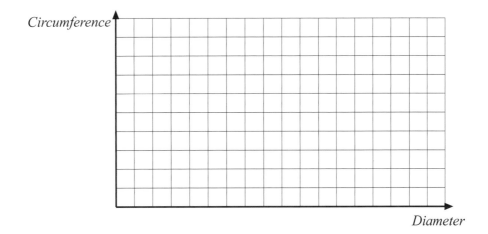

    (b) Explain why a line of best fit should pass through the point with coordinates (0, 0).

    (c) Draw a line of best fit.

    (d) The relationship between the circumference, C, and the diameter, d, is given by $C = kd$, where k is a constant number. Use your line of best fit to determine k.

16.3 Estimating the Area of a Circle

In this section we investigate how the *area* of a circle depends on the *radius* of the circle.

Example 1

Estimate the area of a circle of radius 3 cm.

Solution

The following diagram shows the circle drawn on squared paper. Complete squares are numbered 1 to 16 whilst partial squares are numbered in brackets, e.g. (17), and joined together where possible to approximately make a square, e.g. the two part squares marked (26) add to make about one whole square.

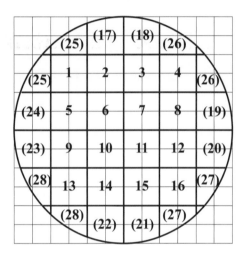

Counting the squares shows that the area is approximately 28 cm^2.

Exercises

1. Draw circles of radius 1 cm, 2 cm, 3 cm, 4 cm, 5 cm, 6 cm and 7 cm on squared paper. Determine the approximate area of each of the circles.

2. What is the area of a circle of radius 0 cm ?

3. (a) Draw a scatter graph to show area against radius for the results that you have obtained in question 1.

   (b) Explain why it would not be sensible to draw a line of best fit through the points that you have plotted.

4. (a) Copy and complete the following table:

Radius (cm)	0	1	2	3	4	5	6	7
(Radius)^2 (cm^2)	0	1		9				
Approximate Area (cm^2)	0			28				

(b) On a set of axes like those shown below, draw a scatter graph using the data from your table.

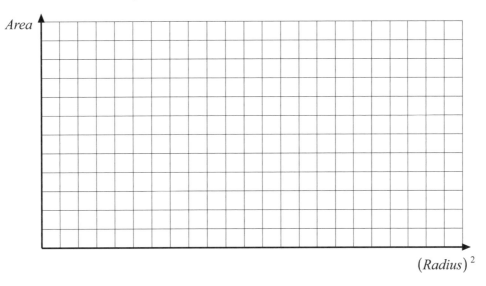

(c) Draw a line of best fit through your data points.

(d) The area, *A*, of a circle of radius *r*, can be found using the formula $A = k r^2$, where *k* is a constant number. Use your line of best fit to determine the value of *k*.

16.4 Formulae for Circumference and Area

In the previous two sections you have found *approximate* formulae for both the circumference and the area of a circle. The *exact* formulae are given below:

$$Circumference = \pi d$$

or

$$Circumference = 2 \pi r$$

$$Area = \pi r^2$$

The symbol π (lower case Greek letter p) represents a special number called 'pi'. The value of π has been calculated to over 1000 million decimal places; its value correct to 5 decimal places is 3.14159.

Compare this with the gradient you obtained from your scatter graphs in the last two sections, to see how close you were.

There is a button on your calculator which you can use when doing calculations involving π, as the next examples illustrate.

Example 1

A circle has radius 6 cm. Calculate:

(a)   its *circumference,*

(b)   its *area.*

Solution

(a)   Circumference $=$ $2 \pi r$

$= 2 \pi \times 6$

$= 37.7$ cm to 3 significant figures.

(b)   Area $=$ πr^2

$= \pi \times 6^2$

$= 113$ cm^2 to 3 significant figures

Example 2

A circle has diameter 7 cm. Calculate:

(a)   its *circumference,*

(b)   its *area.*

Solution

(a)   Circumference $=$ πd

$= \pi \times 7$

$= 22.0$ cm to 3 significant figures.

(b)   Radius $=$ 3.5 cm

Area $=$ πr^2

$= \pi \times 3.5^2$

$= 38.5$ cm^2 to 3 significant figures

Example 3

The circumference of a circle is 18.2 cm. Calculate the length of the diameter, d, of the circle.

Solution

$$C = \pi d$$

$$18.2 = \pi d$$

$$\frac{18.2}{\pi} = d$$

$$d = 5.79 \text{ cm to 3 significant figures.}$$

Example 4

The area of a circle is 22.8 cm^2. Calculate the length of the radius, r, of the circle.

Solution

$$A = \pi r^2$$

$$22.8 = \pi r^2$$

$$\frac{22.8}{\pi} = r^2$$

$$r = \sqrt{\frac{22.8}{\pi}}$$

$$= 2.69 \text{ cm to 3 significant figures.}$$

Exercises

1. A circle has radius 11 cm. Calculate: *to 3 sign figures*

   (a) its diameter, *22 cm*

   (b) its circumference, *πd = 69.*

   (c) its area. *πr^2 121 π = 380*

2. Calculate the circumference and area of a circle with radius 8 cm.

3. Calculate the circumference and area of a circle with diameter 19 cm.

   Circumference = 59.7

   Area = 281

4. Copy and complete the following table:

Radius	Diameter	Circumference	Area
1 2 cm	24 cm	75.4 cm	452 cm
1 cm	2 cm	6.28 cm	3.14 cm
3 mm	6 mm	18.8 mm	28.3 mm
4.5 m	9 m	28.3 m.	63.6 m
11.5 km	23 km	72.3 km.	415 km

5. Determine the circumference and area of the circle shown:

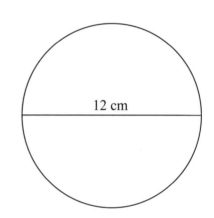

12 cm

6. A circle is cut out of a rectangular piece of card, as shown:

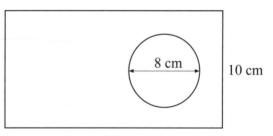

8 cm   10 cm

15 cm

   (a) Calculate the area of the rectangle. 150cm²

   (b) Calculate the area of the circle. 50.3 cm²

   (c) Calculate the area of the card left, when the circle has been cut out. 99.7cm²

7. Calculate the area and perimeter of the semicircle shown:

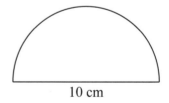

10 cm

39.3 . 25.7 .

8. The circumference of a circle is 29 cm.

   (a) Calculate the radius of the circle.

   (b) Calculate the area of the circle.

9. The area of a circle is 48 cm². Calculate the radius and circumference of the circle.

10. Copy and complete the following table:

Radius	Diameter	Circumference	Area
		82 cm	
			19 m²
	33 m		
		44 mm	
			36 mm²

11. A circle is cut up into sectors that can be placed side-by-side as shown in the following diagram:

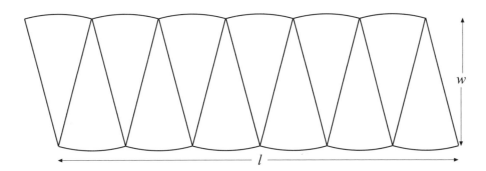

If the angles of the sectors are *very* small, the shape formed almost becomes a rectangle. In this case, *w* is nearly equal to *r*, the radius of the circle.

(a) Explain why *l* is approximately πr.

(b) Use the fact that the shape is close to a rectangle to derive a formula for the area of the circle.

16.5 Problems in Context

In this section we apply the formulae for area and circumference to some problems.

Example 1

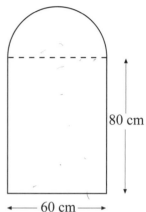

The diagram shows an arched window made in the shape of a semicircle on top of a rectangle. Calculate the area of the window.

Solution

$$\text{Area of rectangle} = 80 \times 60$$

$$= 4800 \text{ cm}^2$$

$$\text{Radius of semicircle} = 30 \text{ cm}$$

$$\text{Area of semicircle} = \frac{1}{2} \times \pi \times 30^2$$

$$= 1414 \text{ cm}^2 \ (4 \text{ s.f.})$$

$$\text{Total area} = 4800 + 1414$$

$$= 6214 \text{ cm}^2 \ (4 \text{ s.f.})$$

Example 2

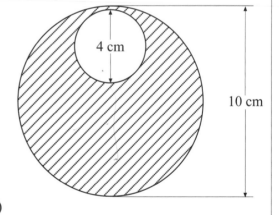

A circular disc of diameter 10 cm has a hole of diameter 4 cm cut in it. Calculate the area remaining of the large disc, as shaded in the diagram.

Solution

$$\text{Radius of large disc} = 5 \text{ cm}$$

$$\text{Area of large disc} = \pi \times 5^2$$

$$= 78.54 \text{ cm}^2 \ (2 \text{ d.p.})$$

$$\text{Radius of hole} = 2 \text{ cm}$$

$$\text{Area of hole} = \pi \times 2^2$$

$$= 12.57 \text{ cm}^2 \ (2 \text{ d.p.})$$

$$\text{Shaded area} = 78.54 - 12.57$$

$$= 65.97 \text{ cm}^2$$

$$\approx 66.0 \text{ cm}^2$$

Example 3

The diagram shows a square with sides of
length 6 cm. A semicircle has been added
to one side of a the square and a quarter of
a circle (quadrant) added to another side.
Calculate the area of the shape.

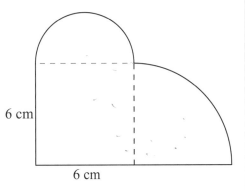

6 cm

6 cm

Solution

Area of square $= 6^2$

$= 36$ cm^2

Radius of semicircle $= 3$ cm

Area of semicircle $= \dfrac{1}{2} \times \pi \times 3^2$

$= 14.1$ cm^2 (3 s.f.)

Radius of quarter circle $= 6$ cm

Area of quadrant $= \dfrac{1}{4} \times \pi \times 6^2$

$= 28.3$ cm^2 (3 s.f.)

Total area $= 36 + 14.1 + 28.3$

$= 78.4$ cm^2 (3 s.f.)

Exercises

28.3 · 14.15
13.5

1. (a) Calculate the area of each part of the following shape:

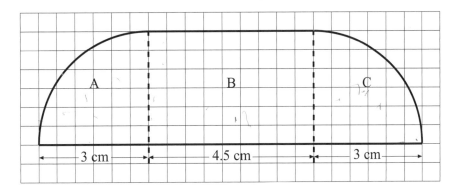

A ≠ C.
$\pi \times 3^2 = 14.14$
B = 45.

(b) What is the *total* area of the shape?

27.78

83

16.5

2. Calculate the area of each of the following shapes:

(a)

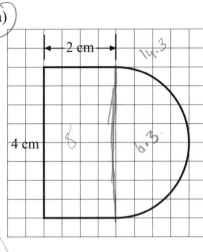

(b)

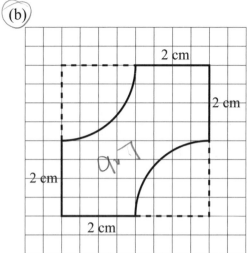

(c)

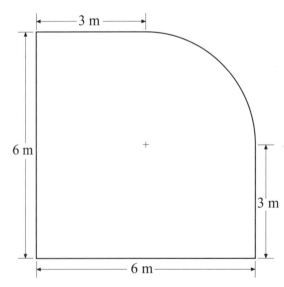

3. The following diagram shows the plan of a patio. Calculate the area of the patio.

4. Calculate the area and perimeter of the following shape:

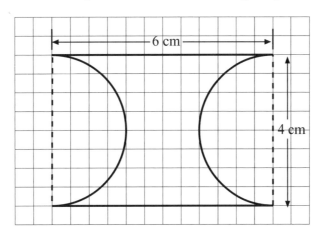

4, 6

5. A Christmas decoration consists of a disc with two holes cut in it, as shown.

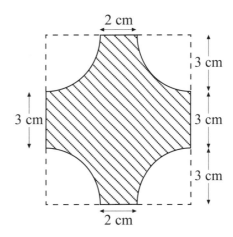

The disc has radius 3.8 cm. 45.4

The large hole has radius 1.2 cm. 4.5

The small hole has radius 0.2 cm. 0.1

Both sides of the decoration are painted.

Calculate the area that is painted.

40.8

6. Calculate the area and perimeter of the shape shown:

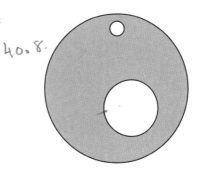

2 cm

3 cm

3 cm

3 cm

3 cm

3 cm

2 cm

7. A set of steps is to be built with a semicircular shape. Three of the steps are shown in the following diagrams. Calculate the area of each of these three steps.

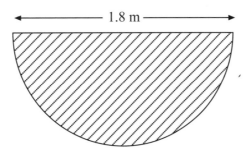

1.8 m

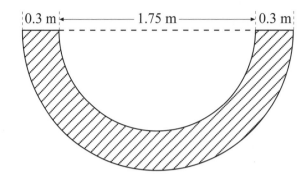

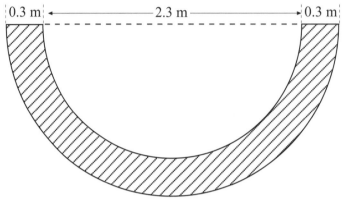

8. A car wheel has radius 0.25 m. How far does the car travel if the wheel goes round:

    (a) 10 times,

    (b) 600 times?

9. A wheel of a bicycle has diameter 60 cm. How many times does the wheel revolve on a journey of length:

    (a) 500 m,

    (b) 2.6 km?

10. Calculate the area and perimeter of the following shapes:

    (a) (b)

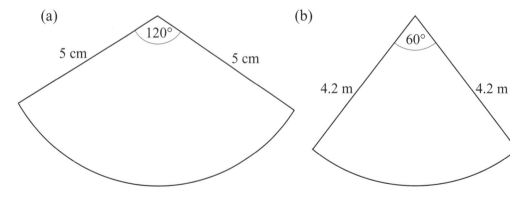

16.6 Volume and Surface Area of a Cylinder

In an earlier unit you will have considered the volume of a *triangular prism*. The formula used for this can be applied to determine the volume of a *cylinder*.

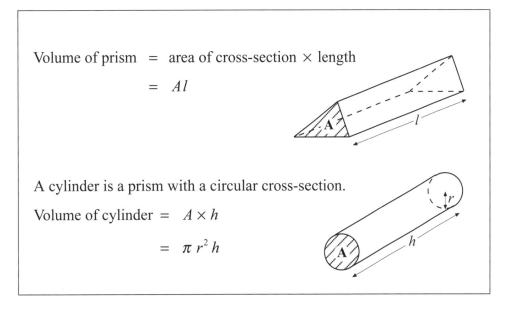

Volume of prism = area of cross-section × length

$$= Al$$

A cylinder is a prism with a circular cross-section.

Volume of cylinder = $A \times h$

$$= \pi r^2 h$$

The total surface area of the cylinder can be determined by splitting it into 3 parts as below:

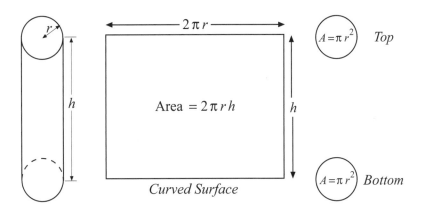

$A = \pi r^2$ *Top*

Area $= 2 \pi r h$

Curved Surface

$A = \pi r^2$ *Bottom*

The curved surface can be opened out to form a rectangle. The length of one side is equal to the height, *h*, of the cylinder; the other is equal to the circumference of the cross-section, $2\pi r$.

Total area = area of curved surface + area of top + area of bottom

$$= 2\pi r h + \pi r^2 + \pi r^2$$

$$= 2\pi r h + 2\pi r^2$$

Example 1

Calculate the volume and surface area of the cylinder shown in the diagram.

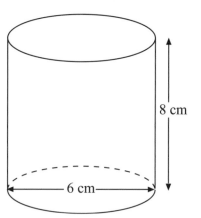

Solution

The radius of the base of the cylinder is 3 cm.

$$\text{Volume} = \pi r^2 h$$
$$= \pi \times 3^2 \times 8$$
$$= 226 \text{ cm}^3 \text{ (3 s.f.)}$$

$$\text{Surface area} = 2\pi rh + 2\pi r^2$$
$$= 2 \times \pi \times 3 \times 8 + 2 \times \pi \times 3^2$$
$$= 207 \text{ cm}^2 \text{ (3 s.f.)}$$

Example 2

The diagram shows a sheet of card that is to be used to make the curved surface of a cylinder of height 8 cm.

(a)   Calculate the radius of the cylinder.

(b)   Use your answer to part (a) to calculate the area of card that would be needed to make ends for the cylinder.

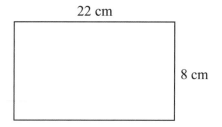

(c)   Calculate the volume of the cylinder.

Solution

(a)   The circumference of the cross-section is 22 cm, so

$$2\pi r = 22$$
$$r = \frac{22}{2\pi}$$
$$= \frac{11}{\pi}$$
$$= 3.50 \text{ cm (3 s.f.)}$$

(b)   Area of ends $= 2 \times \pi r^2$
$$= 2 \times \pi \times 3.50^2$$
$$= 77.0 \text{ cm}^2 \text{ (3 s.f.)}$$

(b)   Volume of cylinder $= \pi r^2 h$
$$= \pi \times 3.5^2 \times 8$$
$$= 308 \text{ cm}^3 \text{ (3 s.f.)}$$

Exercises

1. Calculate the volume of the cylinder shown.

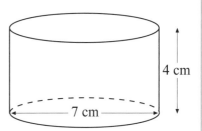

2. Look at the dimensions of the following cylinders:

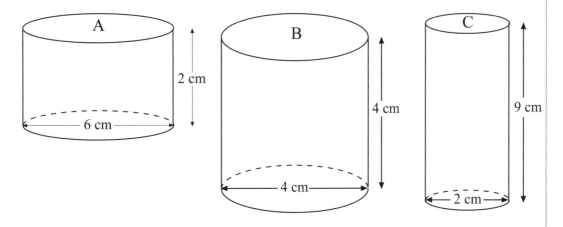

   (a) Without doing any calculations, decide which cylinder you think has the greatest volume.

   (b) Determine the volume of each cylinder and see if you were correct.

3. Calculate the total surface area of the following cylinder:

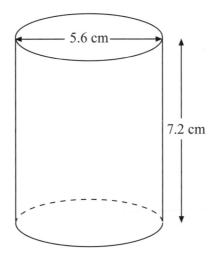

4. The following diagrams show two cylinders, A and B:

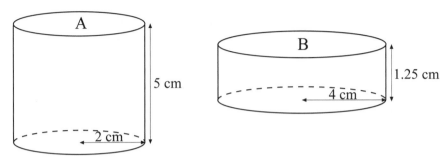

(a) Show that both cylinders have the same volume.

(b) Calculate the total surface area of each cylinder.

5. A cylinder has volume 250 cm^3 and base radius 6 cm.

(a) Calculate the height of the cylinder.

(b) Calculate the total surface area of the cylinder.

6. A cylinder has volume 300 cm^3 and height 9 cm. Calculate the diameter of the cylinder.

7. The curved surface of a cylinder is to be made from a rectangular sheet of material which is 18 cm by 32 cm.

(a) Explain why two different cylinders could be made from this sheet.

(b) Calculate the radius of each of the cylinders.

(c) Calculate the volume of each cylinder.

8. A cylinder has height 11 cm. The area of the curved surface of the cylinder is 40 cm^2. Calculate the volume of the cylinder.

9. The diagram shows the cross-section of a clay pipe. The length of the pipe is 40 cm.

Calculate the volume of clay needed to make the pipe.

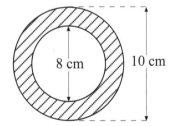

10.

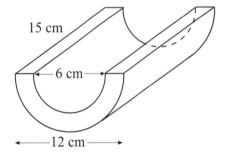

Calculate the volume and the total surface area of the shape shown.

17 Units of Measure

17.1 Estimating Metric Units of Length, Mass and Capacity

It is very useful to be able to *estimate* lengths, masses, etc. because it may not always be easy to measure them. Some useful hints for estimating are listed below:

> The height of a standard door is about 2 m.
>
> The length of an adult pace is about 1 m.
>
> The length of a size 8 shoe is about 30 cm.
>
> Most adults are between 1.5 m and 1.8 m in height.
>
> It takes about 15 minutes to walk one kilometre.
>
> The mass of a standard bag of sugar is 1 kg.
>
> The mass of a family car is about 1 tonne.
>
> 1 hectare $= 10\ 000\ \text{m}^2$ (about 2 football pitches).
>
> A teaspoon holds about 5 ml of liquid.
>
> The volume of a normal can of drink is about $330\ \text{cm}^3$.

Example 1

The diagram shows a tall man standing beside a factory.

Estimate:

(a)   the height of the factory,

(b)   the height of the door.

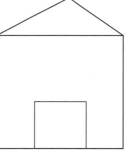

Solution

(a)   The diagram shows that the height of the factory is approximately 5 times the height of the man.

Estimate the man's height as 1.8 m.

An estimate for the height of the factory is

$5 \times 1.8\ \text{m} = 9\ \text{m}$

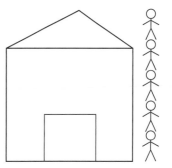

(b)   The height of the door is approximately $1\frac{1}{2}$ times the height of the man.

An estimate for the height of the door is

$$1\frac{1}{2} \times 1.8 = 2.7 \text{ m}$$

Example 2

The diagram shows a tall person standing behind
a lorry.

Estimate the length and height of the lorry, assuming
that the height of the person is about 1.8 m.

Solution

The diagrams show how to make estimates for the
height and length.

Height $\approx$ 2×1.8 m

$\approx$ 3.6 m

Length $\approx$ $3\frac{1}{2} \times 1.8$ m

$\approx$ 6.3 m

Note   If the height of the person was actually 1.6 m, the estimates for the height
and length would change to 3.2 m and 5.6 m respectively.

Exercises

1.   *Estimate* the following in your classroom:

(a)   length of room,

(b)   width of room,

(c)   height of room,

(d)   height of door,

(e)   height of windows,

(f)   width of black/white board.

2.   *Estimate* the following:

    (a)   the height of a football goal,

    (b)   the width of a hockey pitch,

    (c)   the width of a football goal,

    (d)   the height of a netball post.

    Measure the *actual* heights and widths and compare with your estimates.

3.   (a)   *Estimate* the size of your text book (width, height and thickness).

    (b)   *Measure* your text book to see how good your estimates were.

4.   *Estimate* the lengths of the following vehicles:

    (a)   a car,

    (b)   a bus,

    (c)   an articulated lorry,

    (d)   a motorcycle.

5.   Collect together a number of items of various masses.

    (a)   Copy and complete the table, writing in the *actual* mass after each estimate.

Item	Estimate of Mass	Actual Mass
Text book		
Can of drink		

    (b)   Do you become more accurate at estimating as you have more practice?

6.   *Estimate,* in grams or kilograms, the mass of the following:

    (a)   a table tennis ball,

    (b)   a chair,

    (c)   a large dog,

    (d)   your school bag, when full,

    (e)   a calculator,

    (f)   a pen.

7. *Estimate*, in ml or litres, the volume of milk you would:

    (a) add to a cup of tea,

    (b) pour on to cereal in a bowl,

    (c) pour into a mug.

8. *Estimate* the volume of:

    (a) a football,

    (b) a tennis ball,

    (c) a table tennis ball,

    (d) a hockey ball.

9. Jo estimates that the height of a double-decker bus is 9 m. Do you think that this is a reasonable estimate? Explain why.

10. Tony estimates that the capacity of a thermos flask is 1 litre, because it is about the same size and shape as a 1 litre lemonade bottle. Explain whether or not you think he has made a good estimate.

11. Which of the following would be the best estimate for the mass of an apple:

A	1 kg
B	2 grams
C	200 grams
D	20 grams
E	800 grams

12. Which of the following would be the best estimate for the diameter of a saucer:

A	16 cm
B	16 mm
C	16 m
D	8 mm
E	80 cm

13. Which of the following would be the best estimate for the capacity of a tea cup:

A	15 ml
B	1500 ml
C	0.5 litres
D	5 litres
E	150 ml

17.2 The Metric System: Conversion Between Units

The metric (decimal) system uses a number of standard prefixes for units of length, mass, etc.

The three most important are:

$$kilo \quad = \quad 1000$$

$$centi \quad = \quad \frac{1}{100}$$

$$milli \quad = \quad \frac{1}{1000}$$

You will have met many of these already, for example,

1 millimetre	$= \dfrac{1}{1000}$ metre	*so*	1 metre	$=$	1000 millimetres
1 kilogram	$=$ 1000 grams	*so*	1 gram	$= \dfrac{1}{1000}$	kilogram
1 centimetre	$= \dfrac{1}{100}$ metre	*so*	1 metre	$=$	100 centimetres
1 millilitre	$= \dfrac{1}{1000}$ litre	*so*	1 litre	$=$	1000 millilitres

It is also useful to know that:

$$1 \ cm^3 \quad = \quad 1 \ \text{millilitre (ml)}$$

and

$$1000 \ kg = 1 \ \text{tonne}$$

Example 1

Complete each of the following statements:

(a) 150 cm = ☐ m

(b) 360 mm = ☐ m

(c) 3.6 tonnes = ☐ kg

(d) 62 ml = ☐ litres

Solution

(a) $150 \text{ cm} = 150 \times \dfrac{1}{100} = 1.5 \text{ m}$

(b) $360 \text{ mm} = 360 \times \dfrac{1}{1000} = 0.36 \text{ m}$

(c) $3.6 \text{ tonnes} = 3.6 \times 1000 = 3600 \text{ kg}$

(d) $62 \text{ ml} = 62 \times \dfrac{1}{1000} = 0.062 \text{ litres}$

Example 2

John adds 250 ml of water to a jug that already contains 1.2 litres of water. How much water is now in the jug?

Solution

$1.2 \text{ litres} = 1.2 \times 1000$

$= 1200 \text{ ml}$

$\text{Total volume} = 1200 + 250$

$= 1450 \text{ ml or } 1.45 \text{ litres}$

Exercises

1.   Change the following lengths into mm:

(a)	4 cm	(b)	7 cm	(c)	26 cm	(d)	835 cm
(e)	6.2 cm	(f)	14.7 cm	(g)	9.25 cm	(h)	0.04 cm

Change the following lengths into cm:

(i)	60 mm	(j)	80 mm	(k)	340 mm	(l)	9450 mm
(m)	87 mm	(n)	262 mm	(o)	67.9 mm	(p)	6 mm

2.   Change the following lengths into cm:

(a)	7 m	(b)	18 m	(c)	36 m	(d)	904 m
(e)	4.3 m	(f)	53.9 m	(g)	28.38 m	(h)	0.09 m

Change the following lengths into m:

(i)	800 cm	(j)	500 cm	(k)	760 cm	(l)	2150 cm
(m)	365 cm	(n)	57 cm	(o)	77.6 cm	(p)	6 cm

3.   Change the following lengths into m:

(a)   5 km   (b)   11 km   (c)   63 km   (d)   423 km

(e)   7.4 km   (f)   2.56 km   (g)   14.321 km   (h)   0.07 km

Change the following lengths into km:

(i)   6000 m   (j)   17 000 m   (k)   53 000 m   (l)   4750 m

(m)   807 m   (n)   62 m   (o)   3 m   (p)   29.3 m

4.   Change the following masses into g:

(a)   6 kg   (b)   8 kg   (c)   15 kg   (d)   92 kg

(e)   1.7 kg   (f)   5.47 kg   (g)   2.925 kg   (h)   0.004 kg

Change the following masses into kg:

(i)   3000 g   (j)   40 000 g   (k)   8340 g   (l)   29 750 g

(m)   237 g   (n)   52 g   (o)   9 g   (p)   3.6 g

5.   Copy and complete each of the following statements:

(a)   320 mm =   [   ] m   (b)   6420 mm = [   ] m

(c)   642 mm =   [   ] m   (d)   888 cm =   [   ] m

(e)   224 cm =   [   ] mm   (f)   45 m =   [   ] mm

(g)   320 m =   [   ] cm   (h)   8.73 m =   [   ] mm

6.   Convert the following masses to kg:

(a)   8.2 tonnes   (b)   160 tonnes

(c)   88 g   (d)   3470 g

7.   Convert the following masses to g:

(a)   3.6 kg   (b)   3.7 tonnes

(c)   840 mg   (d)   62 mg

8.   Convert the following volumes to ml:

(a) $\frac{1}{4}$ litre   (b)   22 litres

(c)   0.75 litres   (d)   450 cm^3

9. Convert the following volumes to litres:

   (a)   4740 ml   (b)   64 ml

   (c)   300 ml   (d)   3600 cm^3

10. A cake recipe requires 0.25 kg of flour. Rachel has 550 grams of flour.
    How much flour will she have left when she has made the cake? Give your
    answer

    (a)   in kg,   (b)   in g.

11. A chemistry teacher requires 250 mg of a chemical for an experiment. He
    has 30 grams of the chemical. How many times can he carry out the
    experiment?

12. A bottle contains 1.5 litres of cola. Hannah drinks 300 ml of the cola and
    then Ben drinks 450 ml. How much of the cola is left? Give your answer

    (a)   in ml,   (b)   in litres.

13. Emma estimates that the mass of one sweet is 20 grams. How many sweets
    would you expect to find in a packet that contains 0.36 kg of these sweets?

14. To make a certain solution, 50 grams of a chemical must be dissolved in
    4 litres of water.

    (a)   How much of the chemical should be dissolved in 1 litre of water?

    (b)   How many ml of water would be needed for 200 mg of the chemical?

    (c)   How many grams of the chemical would be dissolved in 500 ml of
          water?

17.3 Estimating Imperial Units of Length, Mass and Capacity

The imperial system was used, until very recently, for *all* weights and measures
throughout the UK. There are many aspects of everyday life where the system is
still in common usage. Road signs are an obvious example where miles instead of
kilometres are used. In this section we look at estimating in these units; the
following list gives some useful facts to help you.

> The height of a tall adult is about 6 feet.
>
> The width of an adult thumb is about 1 inch.
>
> The length of a size 8 shoe is about 1 foot.
>
> An adult pace is about 1 yard.
>
> The mass of a bag of sugar is just over 2 pounds.
>
> An old-style bottle of milk contains 1 pint.
>
> It takes about 20 minutes to walk one mile.

You will find the following abbreviations used for imperial units:

1 yard = 1 yd		6 feet = 6 ft = 6 '	
9 inches = 9 in = 9 "		8 ounces = 8 oz	
7 pounds = 7 lb			

but be careful not to use m as an abbreviation for miles because m is a standard abbreviation for metres.

Example 1

Estimate the length of the following line, in inches:

Solution

The diagram shows the line itself and the outline of 4 adult thumbs:

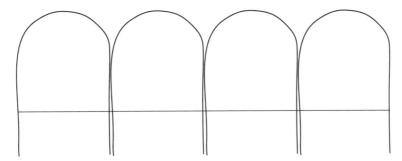

So the length can be estimated as 4 inches.

Example 2

The picture shows a man standing next to a wall with a gate in it:

Estimate the height in feet of both the wall and the gate.

Solution

The wall is about $1\frac{1}{3}$ times the height of the man, so taking the height of the man as 6 feet, gives

$$\text{height of wall} \approx 1\frac{1}{3} \times 6 \approx 8 \text{ feet}$$

The gate is about the same height as the man, so its height can be estimated as six feet.

Exercises

1. *Estimate* the length of each of the lines below, in inches. Then *measure* each line to check your estimate.

    (a) _____

    (b)   _____

    (c)   _____

    (d)   _____

2. (a) *Estimate* the size of the top of your desk, in inches.

    (b) *Measure* your desk and see how accurate your estimate was.

3. (a) *Estimate* the heights of 4 of your friends, in feet and inches.

    (b) *Measure* these friends and see how accurate your estimates were.

4. *Estimate* the length and width of your classroom, in feet.

5. *Estimate* the total mass of 3 maths text books, in pounds.

6. *Estimate* the mass of an apple, in ounces. (Remember that there are 16 ounces in 1 lb.)

7. *Estimate* the capacity of a mug, in pints.

8.   *Estimate* the mass of your shoe, in pounds. Check your estimate if possible.

9.   *Estimate* the dimensions of a football or hockey pitch, in yards.

10.   A fish tank is in the shape of a cube with sides of length 1 foot. *Estimate* the volume of this tank in pints.

17.4 Metric and Imperial Units

As both metric and imperial units are in general use, you need to be able to convert between the two systems. The list below contains a number of useful conversion facts which you will need in the examples and exercises that follow.

8 km	≈	5 miles
1 m	≈	40 inches
30 cm	≈	1 foot
2.5 cm	≈	1 inch
1 kg	≈	2.2 lbs
1 litre	≈	$1\frac{3}{4}$ pints
1 gallon	≈	$4\frac{1}{2}$ litres
1 acre	≈	$\frac{2}{5}$ hectare
450 g	≈	1 lb

The following list reminds you of some of the relationships in the imperial system:

1 lb	=	16 ounces
1 stone	=	14 lb
1 mile	=	1760 yards
1 yard	=	3 feet
1 foot	=	12 inches
1 gallon	=	8 pints
1 chain	=	22 yards
1 furlong	=	220 yards

Also note that   1 acre =   4840 square yards (approximately the
                                                           area of a football pitch)

Conversions between metric and imperial units are not precise, so we always
round the converted figure, taking the context into account (see Examples 1 and 2
below).

Example 1

While on holiday in France, a family see the following road-sign:

PARIS   342 km

How many *miles* are the family from Paris?

Solution

Note   8 km ≈ 5 miles

Distance from Paris   ≈ $342 \times \dfrac{5}{8}$ miles

$\qquad\qquad\qquad\qquad ≈ \ 213.75$ miles

The family are therefore about 214 miles from Paris.

Example 2

A bottle contains 2.5 litres of milk. How many *pints* of milk does the bottle
contain?

Solution

Note   1 litre ≈ $1\dfrac{3}{4}$ pints

Volume of milk   ≈ 2.5×1.75 pints

$\qquad\qquad\qquad ≈ \ 4.375$ pints

The bottle contains almost $4\dfrac{1}{2}$ pints of milk.

Example 3

Vera buys 27 litres of petrol for her car. How many *gallons* of petrol does she
buy?

Solution

Note   1 gallon   ≈ 4.5 litres

Quantity of petrol   ≈ $\dfrac{27}{4.5}$

   ≈ 6 gallons

Vera buys approximately 6 gallons of petrol.

Exercises

1.   Change the following lengths into inches:

    (a)   4 feet   (b)   7 feet   (c)   4 feet 2 inches

    (d)   8 feet 7 inches   (e)   5.5 feet   (f)   2 yards

    (g)   5 yards 2 feet   (h)   1 mile

    Change the following lengths into feet or feet and inches:

    (i)   60 inches   (j)   48 inches   (k)   17 inches

    (l)   29 inches   (m)   108 inches   (n)   95 inches

    (o)   240 inches   (p)   6 inches

2.   Change the following masses into ounces:

    (a)   7 pounds   (b)   11 pounds   (c)   36 pounds

    (d)   904 pounds   (e)   42 pounds   (f)   5.5 pounds

    (g)   2 stone   (h)   9 stone 12 pounds

    Change the following masses into pounds or pounds and ounces:

    (i)   80 ounces   (j)   128 ounces   (k)   56 ounces

    (l)   720 ounces   (m)   36 ounces   (n)   77 ounces

    (o)   8 ounces   (p)   4 ounces

3.   Change the following volumes into pints:

    (a)   5 gallons   (b)   11 gallons   (c)   63 gallons

    (d)   412 gallons   (e)   7.5 gallons   (f) $\dfrac{1}{2}$ gallon

    (g) $3\dfrac{1}{4}$ gallons   (h)   6.875 gallons

Change the following volumes into gallons or gallons and pints:

(i)   56 pints   (j)   160 pints   (k)   4800 pints

(l)   528 pints   (m)   12 pints   (n)   87 pints

(o)   2 pints   (p)   1884 pints

4.   Convert the following distances to cm, where necessary giving your answers to 2 significant figures where necessary:

(a)   6 inches   (b)   8 inches   (c) $7\frac{1}{2}$ inches

(d)   8 feet   (e)   4 yards   (f) $1\frac{1}{4}$ yards

5.   The road-sign shown gives distances in km:

Produce a version of the sign with the equivalent distances given in *miles*.

BREST	400
ROSCOFF	384
ST MALO	168
RENNES	162
NANTES	148

6.   A recipe requires $\frac{1}{2}$ lb of flour. What is the equivalent amount of flour in:

(a)   grams,   (b)   kilograms,   (c)   ounces ?

7.   The capacity of a fuel tank is 30 gallons. What is the capacity of the tank in:

(a)   litres,   (b)   pints ?

8.   A cow produces an average of 18 pints of milk each time she is milked. Convert this to *litres*, giving your answer to 1 decimal place.

9.   The mass of a parcel is 4 lb 4 oz. Calculate its mass in kilograms, giving your answer to 1 decimal place.

10.   Copy and complete the table shown, which can be used to convert speeds between mph and km/h. Where necessary, express your answers to 3 significant figures.

mph	km/h
30	
	50
40	
	70
	80
60	
	100
70	
	120

11. A recipe book provides a table for the conversion between ounces and grams.

    Copy and complete the table, where necessary giving the values correct to 1 decimal place.

Ounces	Grams
	20
1	
	50
2	
	100
4	
8	
9	
	300
	400

12. (a) Julie calculates the number of metres in 1 mile like this:

    $$1760 \times 3 \times 0.3 = 1584$$

    Jill calculates the number of metres in 1 mile like this:

    $$\frac{8 \times 1000}{5} = 1600$$

    Describe how the two methods work and explain why they give different answers.

    (b) Show two different ways of converting 20 litres to gallons.

13. The heights of 4 children are measured in feet and inches.

    (a) Convert these heights to cm:

    Ben   5 ' 4 "   Rachel   5 ' 8 "

    Emma 4 ' 7 "   Hannah 3 ' 1 "

    (b) Calculate the mean height of the four children,

    (i)   in cm   (ii)   in feet and inches.

17.5 Problems in Context

In this section we look at a variety of problems where the context requires us to deal with more than one type of unit. The units may be only metric, or only imperial, or a mixture of both.

Example 1

A school canteen buys a 1 gallon can of fruit juice. The canteen sells the fruit juice in paper cups that each contain 150 ml of drink. How many cups can be filled?

Solution

1 gallon $\approx$ 4.5 litres

$\quad\quad\quad\ \approx$ 4500 ml

So about $\dfrac{4500}{150}$ = 30 cups can be filled from one can.

Example 2

Some students take part in a 20-mile sponsored relay run, where each student runs 3000 m and then another student takes over. If each student runs only once, how many students are needed to complete the run?

Solution

20 miles $\approx$ $20 \times \dfrac{8}{5}$ km

$\quad\quad\quad\ \approx$ 32 km

$\quad\quad\quad\ \approx$ 32 000 m

$32\,000 \div 3000$ = 10 remainder 2000,

so 11 students are needed to complete the run, but one of them will run only about 2000 m.

Example 3

A technology teacher has a 50-yard roll of glass fibre tape. For a project, each student in the class will need 80 cm of tape. There are 30 students in the class. What length of tape will be left over?

Solution

$50 \text{ yards} = 50 \times 3$

$= 150 \text{ feet}$

$\approx 150 \times 0.3 \text{ m}$

$\approx 45 \text{ m}$

$\text{Tape used} = 30 \times 80 \text{ cm}$

$= 2400 \text{ cm}$

$= 24 \text{ m}$

$\text{Tape left} \approx 45 - 24 \text{ m}$

$\approx 21 \text{ m}$

Exercises

1. A glass holds 50 ml of drink. How many glasses can be filled from:

    (a) a 1 litre bottle,

    (b) a 1 gallon can,

    (c) a 3 pint carton ?

2. A sheet of wood measures 4 feet by 8 feet. A teacher cuts up the sheet into smaller pieces that measure 10 cm by 20 cm. How many of these smaller sheets can the teacher make?

3. A baker buys a 25 kg sack of flour. He uses 1 lb of flour for each loaf. How many loaves can he make with 1 sack of flour?

4. How many 125 ml glasses can be filled from a can that contains 2 pints of milk?

5. How many books of width 2.5 cm can be put on a shelf of length 3 feet?

6. A ball of wool contains 75 yards. If 22 m are needed for a knitting pattern, what length of wool is left? Give your answer in:

    (a)   metres,   (b)   yards,   (c)   feet and inches.

7.   If the average length of a car is 4 m, determine the length of a bumper-to-bumper traffic jam containing 2000 cars, in:

(a)   km,   (b)   miles.

8.   The length of a domino is 2 inches. A group of children placed dominoes end-to-end to form a line of length 100 m. How many dominoes did they use?

9.   The diameter of a bicycle wheel is 28 inches. How many times would the wheel go round as the bicycle moves:

(a)   550 yards,   (b)   1 mile,   (c)   1 km ?

10. The mass of 1 litre of water is 1 kg. Determine the mass of:

(a)   1 pint of water, in ounces,

(b)   1 gallon of water, in pounds,

(c)   50 ml of water, in ounces.

18 Speed, Distance and Time

18.1 Speed

In this section we introduce the idea of speed, considering both *instantaneous speed* and *average speed*.

Instantaneous speed $\quad = \quad$ speed at any instant in time

$$\text{Average speed} \quad = \quad \frac{\text{distance travelled}}{\text{time taken}}$$

If a car travels 100 miles in 2 hours,

$$\text{average speed} \quad = \quad \frac{100}{2}$$

$$= \quad 50 \text{ mph}$$

The car does not travel at a constant speed of 50 mph; its speed varies during the journey between 0 mph and, perhaps, 70 mph. The speed at any time is called the *instantaneous speed*.

The following table lists units in common use for speed and their abbreviations:

Distance	*Time*	*Speed*	*Abbreviation*
mile	hours	miles per hour	mph
kilometres	hours	kilometres per hour	km/h
metres	hours	metres per hour	m/h
metres	seconds	metres per second	m/s
feet	seconds	feet per second	f.p.s. *or* ft. per sec.
centimetres	seconds	centimetres per second	cm/sec *or* cm/s

Example 1

Judith drives from Plymouth to Southampton, a distance of 160 miles, in 4 hours.

She then drives from Southampton to London, a distance of 90 miles, in 1 hour and 30 minutes.

Determine her average speed for each journey.

Solution

| Plymouth to Southampton | Average speed | $= \dfrac{160}{4}$ |

$$= 40 \text{ mph}$$

Southampton to London　　Time taken　$=$ 1 hour and 30 minutes

$$= 1\tfrac{1}{2} \text{ hours } \textit{or } \tfrac{3}{2} \text{ hours}$$

$$\text{Average speed} = 90 \div \tfrac{3}{2}$$

$$= 90 \times \tfrac{2}{3}$$

$$= 60 \text{ mph}$$

Example 2

John can type 960 words in 20 minutes.

Calculate his typing speed in:

(a)　words per minute,

(b)　words per hour.

Solution

(a)　Typing speed　$= \dfrac{960}{20}$

$$= 48 \text{ words per minute}$$

(b)　Typing speed　$= 48 \times 60$

$$= 2880 \text{ words per hour}$$

Exercises

1. Peter drives 320 miles in 8 hours. Calculate his average speed.

2. Daisy drives from Sheffield to London, a distance of 168 miles, in 4 hours. Calculate her average speed.

3. A snail moves 8 m in 2 hours. Calculate the average speed of the snail in metres per hour.

4. A lorry driver keeps a record of each journey he makes. Calculate the average speed for each journey, using the table below:

Start	Finish	Start Time	Finish Time	Distance
Brighton	Norwich	0800	1200	172 miles
Norwich	Carlisle	1400	1900	280 miles
Carlisle	Cardiff	1000	1800	300 miles
Cardiff	Exeter	0700	0930	120 miles
Exeter	Brighton	1030	1530	175 miles

5. Javinda takes $1\frac{1}{2}$ hours to drive 30 km in the rush hour. Calculate his average speed in km/h.

6. Rebecca cycles 20 miles on her bike in 2 hours and 30 minutes. Calculate her average speed in mph.

7. Julie can type 50 words in 2 minutes.
    Debbie can type 300 words in 15 minutes.

    Calculate the typing speed of each of the girls in:

    (a)   words per minute,

    (b)   words per hour.

8. Fatima, Emma and Andy each drive from London to Brighton, a distance of 60 miles. Fatima takes 1 hour, Emma takes 2 hours and Andy takes $1\frac{1}{2}$ hours. Calculate the average speed for each of the drivers.

9. Eva drives from Edinburgh to Dover in 3 stages:

	Start Time	Finish Time	Distance
Edinburgh to Leeds	0620	0920	210 miles
Leeds to London	1035	1305	200 miles
London to Dover	1503	1703	78 miles

Calculate her average speed for each stage of her journey.

10. Delia drives 220 km in $3\frac{1}{2}$ hours. Calculate her average speed correct to the nearest km/h.

18.2 Calculating Speed, Distance and Time

In this section we extend the ideas of speed to calculating *distances* and *times*, using the following formulae:

$$\text{Speed} = \frac{\text{Distance}}{\text{Time}}$$

$$\text{Distance} = \text{Speed} \times \text{Time}$$

$$\text{Time} = \frac{\text{Distance}}{\text{Speed}}$$

Example 1

Jane drives at an average speed of 45 mph on a journey of 135 miles. How long does the journey take?

Solution

$$\text{Time} = \frac{\text{distance}}{\text{speed}}$$

$$= \frac{135}{45}$$

$$= 3 \text{ hours}$$

Example 2

Chris cycles at an average speed of 8 mph. If he cycles for $6\frac{1}{2}$ hours, how far does he travel?

Solution

Distance $=$ speed $\times$ time

$$= 8 \times 6\frac{1}{2}$$

$$= 52 \text{ miles}$$

Example 3

Nikki has to travel a total of 351 miles. She travels the first 216 miles in 4 hours.

(a) Calculate her average speed for the first part of the journey.

(b) If her average speed remains the same, calculate the total time for the complete journey.

Solution

(a) Average speed $= \dfrac{\text{distance}}{\text{time}}$

$$= \dfrac{216}{4}$$

$$= 54 \text{ mph}$$

(b) Time $= \dfrac{\text{distance}}{\text{speed}}$

$$= \dfrac{351}{54}$$

$$= 6.5 \text{ hours}$$

Exercises

1. Calculate the distance that you would travel if you drove for:

   (a) 3 hours at 20 mph

   (b) 8 hours at 60 mph

   (c) $\frac{1}{2}$ hour at 76 mph

   (d) $1\frac{1}{2}$ hours at 42 mph

   (e) $6\frac{1}{4}$ hours at 40 mph

   (f) 30 minutes at 33 mph

   (g) 45 minutes at 60 mph

   (h) 90 minutes at 45 mph

2. How long does it take to travel:

   (a) 120 miles at 40 mph

   (b) 300 miles at 50 mph

   (c) 240 miles at 60 mph

   (d) 385 miles at 70 mph

   (e) 60 miles at 40 mph

   (f) 360 miles at 30 mph

   (g) 390 miles at 60 mph

   (h) 253 miles at 46 mph

3. A car travels 300 miles in 5 hours. Calculate the average speed of the car in:

   (a) mph,

   (b) miles per minute.

   How long does it take for the car to travel 82 miles?

4. Janet and Bill leave their home at the same time. Janet has 60 miles to travel and drives at 40 mph. Bill has 80 miles to travel and also drives at 40 mph.

   (a) How long does Janet's journey take?

   (b) How much longer does Bill spend driving than Janet?

5. An athlete can run long distances at 4 metres per second. How far can she run in:

   (a) 50 seconds,

   (b) 3 minutes,

   (c) 1 hour,

   (d) $2\frac{1}{2}$ hours ?

6. Andrew rows at an average speed of 2 metres per second.

   (a) How long does it take him to row:

   (i) 70 m,   (ii) 800 m,   (iii) $1\frac{1}{2}$ km ?

(b)   How far can Andrew row in:

   (i)   12 seconds,   (ii) $3\frac{1}{2}$ minutes,   (iii)   4 hours ?

7.   A snail moves 5 m in 2 hours, If the snail moves at the same speed, calculate:

   (a)   the time it takes to move 20 m,

   (b)   the distance it would move in $3\frac{1}{2}$ hours,

   (c)   the time it takes to moves 1 m,

   (d)   the distance that it moves in 15 minutes.

8.   Laura drives for 3 hours at 44 mph.
    Clare drives 144 miles in 4 hours.

   (a)   Who travels the greater distance?

   (b)   Whose speed is the slower?

   (c)   How far would Laura travel if she drove for 3 hours at the same speed as Clare?

9.   A lorry travels for 3 hours at 48 mph and then for 2 hours at 53 mph.

   (a)   What is the total distance travelled by the lorry?

   (b)   What is the average speed for the whole journey?

10.   Sally drives for $2\frac{1}{2}$ hours at 50 mph, then drives 80 miles at 40 mph, and finally drives for 30 minutes at 60 mph.

   (a)   Calculate the total distance that Sally drives.

   (b)   Calculate the time that Sally takes for the journey.

   (c)   Calculate her average speed for the whole journey.

18.3   Problems with Mixed Units

In this section we consider working with mixed units, and with changing units used for speeds.

Example 1

(a)   Convert 1 hour 24 minutes to hours (decimal).

(b)   Write 2.32 hours in hours and minutes.

Solution

(a) $\dfrac{24}{60} = 0.4$

Therefore,

$$1 \text{ hr } 24 \text{ mins } = 1.4 \text{ hours}$$

(b) $0.32 \times 60 = 19.2$

Therefore,

$$2.32 \text{ hours } = 2 \text{ hrs } 19.2 \text{ mins}$$

Example 2

A car travels 200 miles in 3 hours and 20 minutes. Calculate the average speed of the car in mph.

Solution

$$3 \text{ hours } 20 \text{ minutes } = 3\dfrac{20}{60}$$

$$= 3\dfrac{1}{3} \text{ hours}$$

$$\begin{aligned}
\text{Speed } &= \text{ distance } \div \text{ time} \\
&= 200 \div 3\dfrac{1}{3} \\
&= 200 \div \dfrac{10}{3} \\
&= 200 \times \dfrac{3}{10} \\
&= 60 \text{ mph}
\end{aligned}$$

Example 3

An athlete runs 1500 m in 3 minutes and 12 seconds. Calculate the average speed of the athlete in m/s.

Solution

$$3 \text{ minutes } 12 \text{ seconds } = 3 \times 60 + 12$$

$$= 192 \text{ seconds}$$

$$\text{Speed} = \frac{\text{distance}}{\text{time}}$$

$$= \frac{1500}{192}$$

$$= 7.8 \text{ m/s to 1 decimal place}$$

Example 4

A bus travels at a speed of 40 km/h. Calculate the speed of the bus in:

(a)   m/s

(b)   mph.

Solution

(a)   1 km = 1000 m

$$40 \text{ km/h} = 1000 \times 40 \text{ m/hr}$$

$$1 \text{ hour} = 60 \times 60$$

$$= 3600 \text{ seconds}$$

$$40 \text{ km/h} = \frac{1000 \times 40}{3600}$$

$$= 11.1 \text{ m/s to 1 decimal place}$$

(b) $1 \text{ km} = \dfrac{5}{8} \text{ mile}$

So $40 \text{ km/h} = \dfrac{5}{8} \times 40$

$$= 25 \text{ mph}$$

Example 5

Convert a speed of 8 m/s to mph.

Solution

$$8 \text{ m/s} = 8 \times 3600 \text{ m/h}$$

$$= 28\ 800 \text{ m/h}$$

$$= 28.8 \text{ km/h}$$

$$28.8 \times \frac{5}{8} = 18 \text{ mph}$$

Exercises

1. Convert the following times from hours and minutes to hours, giving your answers as mixed numbers and decimals, correct to 2 decimal places.

   (a) 1 hour 40 minutes   (b) 3 hours 10 minutes

   (c) 1 hour 6 minutes   (d) 2 hours 18 minutes

   (e) 3 hours 5 minutes   (f) 6 hours 2 minutes

   (g) 1 hour 7 minutes   (h) 2 hours 23 minutes

2. Change the following times to hours and minutes:

   (a) $1\frac{1}{4}$ hours   (b) 1.2 hours

   (c) 3.7 hours   (d) 4.4 hours

   (e) 1.45 hours   (f) 3.65 hours

3. A car travels 60 miles in 50 minutes. Calculate the average speed of the car in mph.

4. Jane drives 80 miles in 1 hour and 40 minutes. Calculate her average speed.

5. Convert the following speeds to km/h:

   (a) 60 mph   (b) 43 m/s

   (c) 66 m/s   (d) 84 mph

6. Convert the following speeds to mph:

   (a) 16 m/s   (b) 82 km/h

   (c) 48 km/h   (d) 7 m/s

7. Alec drives 162 km in 2 hours and 12 minutes. Calculate his average speed in:

   (a) km/h   (b) m/s   (c) mph

   Give your answers to 2 decimal places.

8. Jai drives 297 miles in 5 hours and 24 minutes.

   (a) Calculate his average speed in mph.

   (b) He then drives for a further 1 hour and 28 minutes at the same average speed. How far has he travelled altogether?

   Give your answers to 2 decimal places.

9.   A train travels at 40 m/s. Calculate the time it takes to travel:

       (a)   30 000 m,

       (b)   50 km,

       (c)   200 miles.

10.   A long distance runner runs at an average speed of 7 mph. How long will it take the runner to run:

       (a)   20 miles,

       (b)   15 km,

       (c)   10 000 m ?

18.4 Distance-Time Graphs

Graphs that show distance against time can be used to describe journeys. The vertical scale shows the distance from the starting point or reference point.

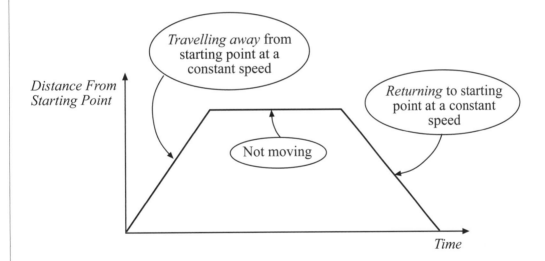

The graph above illustrates 3 parts of a journey.

The *gradient of a straight line* gives the *speed* of the moving object.

Gradient is a measure of the speed.

Note that a *negative gradient* indicates that the object is moving *towards the starting point* rather than away from it.

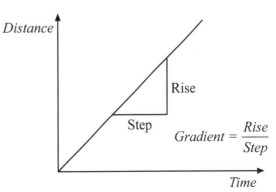

Example 1

The graph shows how far a child is from home.

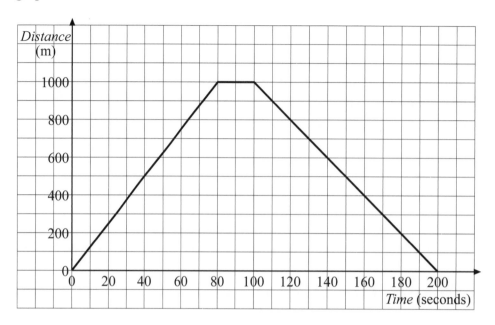

(a)   Describe how the child moves.

(b)   Calculate the speed of the child on each part of the journey.

Solution

(a)   The first part of the graph shows the child moving away from home at a constant speed.

The second (horizontal) part of the graph shows that the child remains in the same position.

The third part of the graph shows the child returning to the starting point at a steady speed.

(b)   During the first stage the child travels 1000 m in 80 seconds.

$$\text{Speed} = \frac{\text{distance}}{\text{time}}$$

$$= \frac{1000}{80}$$

$$= 12.5 \text{ m/s}$$

During the second stage the speed of the child is zero.

During the third stage as the child returns, he travels 1000 m in 100 seconds.

$$\text{Speed} = \frac{\text{distance}}{\text{time}}$$

$$= \frac{1000}{100}$$

$$= 10 \text{ m/s}$$

Example 2

On a journey, Rebecca drives at 50 mph for 2 hours, rests for 1 hour and then drives another 70 miles in $1\frac{1}{2}$ hours.

Draw a distance-time graph to illustrate this journey.

Solution

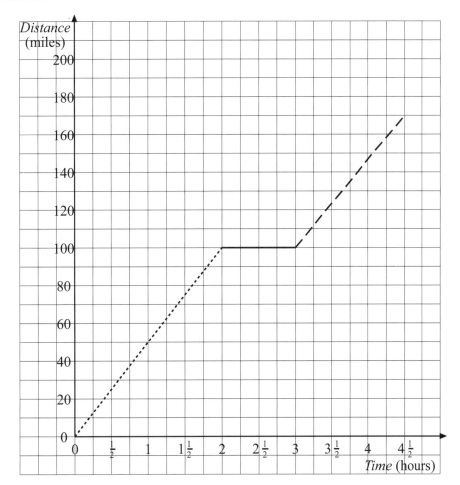

First stage ·······

Travels 100 miles in 2 hours.

Second stage ——

Rests, so distance does not change.

Third stage — — —

Travels 70 miles in $1\frac{1}{2}$ hours.

Example 3

The graph shows how Tom's distance from home varies with time, when he visits Ian.

(a)   How long does Tom spend at Ian's?

(b)   How far is it from Tom's home to Ian's?

(c)   For how long does Tom stop on the way to Ian's?

(d)   On which part of the journey does Tom travel the fastest?

(e)   How fast does Tom walk on the way back from Ian's?

Solution

(a)   The longer horizontal part of the graph represents the time that Tom is at Ian's.

Time =   90 – 40

          =   50 minutes

(b)   3000 m

(c)   Tom stops for 10 minutes, represented by the smaller horizontal part on the graph.

(d)   He travels fastest on the second part of the journey to Ian's. This is where the graph is steepest. He travels 2000 m in 10 minutes.

$$\text{Speed} = \frac{2000}{10}$$

$$= 200 \text{ m/minute}$$

$$= \frac{200 \times 60}{1000}$$

$$= 12 \text{ km/h}$$

(e)   Tom travels 3000 m in 30 mins.

$$Speed = \frac{distance}{time}$$

$$= \frac{3000}{30}$$

$$= 100 \text{ m/minute}$$

Exercises

1.   The following graph illustrates how Jamil moves as he goes to the paper shop:

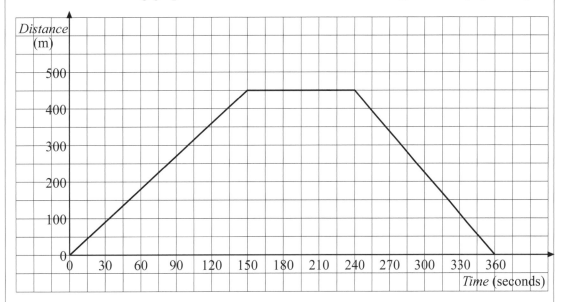

(a)   How long does it take Jamil to cycle to the shop?

(b)   What distance does Jamil cycle to get to the shop?

(c)   Calculate the speed at which Jamil cycles to the shop.

(d)   How long does Jamil spend at the shop?

(e)   Calculate the speed at which Jamil cycles on his way home.

2.   On a journey, Vera

• drives 200 miles in 4 hours

• rests for 1 hour

• drives another 100 miles in 2 hours.

Draw a distance-time graph for Vera's journey.

3. Describe the 5 parts of the journey (labelled (a), (b), (c), (d) and (e)) represented by the following distance-time graph:

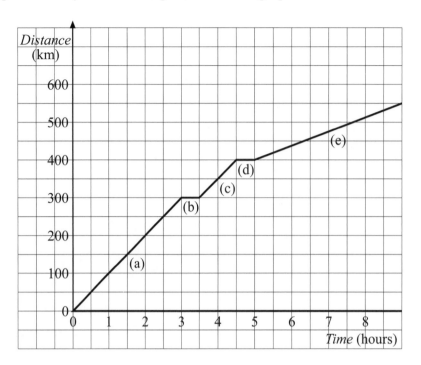

4. Ray walks 420 m from his house to a shop in 7 minutes. He spends 5 minutes at the shop and then walks home in 6 minutes.

    (a)   Draw a distance-time graph for Ray's shopping trip.

    (b)   Calculate the speed at which Ray walks on each part of the journey.

5. Mary sprints 200 m in 30 seconds, rests for 45 seconds and then walks back in $1\frac{1}{2}$ minutes to where she started the race.

    (a)   Draw a distance-time graph for Mary.

    (b)   Calculate the speed at which Mary runs.

    (c)   Calculate the speed at which Mary walks.

6. After morning school, Mike walks home from school to have his lunch. The distance-time graph on the next page describes his journey on one day, showing his distance from home.

    (a)   How far is Mike's home from school?

    (b)   How long does it take Mike to walk home?

    (c)   At what speed does he walk on the way home? Give your answer in m/s.

    (d)   How long does Mike spend at home?

(e)   At what speed does he walk back to school? Give your answer in m/s.

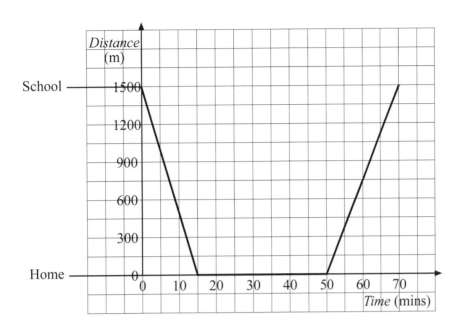

7.   Helen cycles for 20 minutes at 5 m/s and then for a further 10 minutes at 4 m/s.

(a)   How far does she cycle altogether?

(b)   Draw a distance-time graph for her ride.

8.   The distance-time graph shown is for a 3000 m cross-country race, run by Rachel and James.

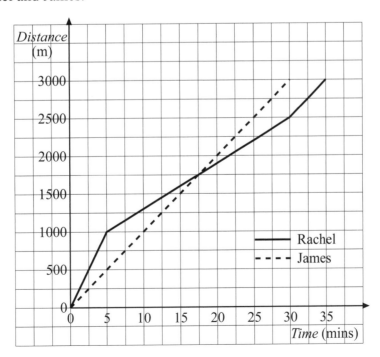

(a)   Describe how James runs the race.

(b)   Describe how Rachel runs the race.

(c)   When, and how far from the start, does James catch up with Rachel?

(d)   Calculate the speed at which James runs.

(e)   Calculate the different speeds at which Rachel runs.

(f)   Who wins the race?

9.   Josh completes a 10 000 m race. He runs the first 2000 m at 5 m/s, the next 7400 m at 4 m/s and the last 600 m at 6 m/s.

    (a)   Draw a distance-time graph for Josh's race.

    (b)   How long does he take to complete the race?

10.   Emma runs a 2000 m race. She runs at 5 m/s for the first part of the race and at 4 m/s for the rest of the race. She complete the race in 440 seconds.

    (a)   Draw a distance-time graph for Emma's race.

    (b)   How far does she run at each speed?

11.   Describe the journey shown in each of the following graphs:

(a)

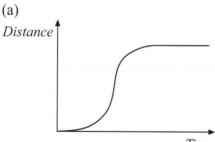

(b)

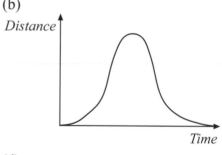

(c)

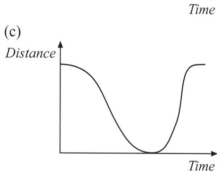

(d)

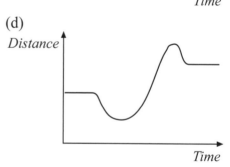

18.5 Other Compound Measures

In the section so far we have considered speed in several different contexts. We will now look at other things such as goals per game, and postage rates.

Example 1

In a football season, Ivor Boot scores 27 goals in 40 matches. Calculate his average scoring rate in goals per match, goals per minute and goals per hour.

Solution

Scoring rate $= \dfrac{27}{40}$

$\qquad\qquad = 0.675$ goals per match

Scoring rate $= \dfrac{27}{40 \times 90}$ (there are 90 minutes per match)

$\qquad\qquad = 0.0075$ goals per minute

Scoring rate $= \dfrac{27}{40 \times 1\frac{1}{2}}$

$\qquad\qquad = 0.45$ goals per hour

Example 2

A package has a mass of 200 grams. It can be posted first class for 60p, or second class for 47p. Calculate the cost per gram for first and second class post.

Solution

First Class   Cost per gram $= \dfrac{60}{200}$

$\qquad\qquad\qquad\qquad = 0.3p$

Second Class   Cost per gram $= \dfrac{47}{200}$

$\qquad\qquad\qquad\qquad = 0.235p$

Exercises

1. Three boys play football for a school team. The numbers of goals scored and matches played are listed below:

	Number of Goals Scored	*Number of Matches Played*
Ian	16	32
Ben	22	40
Sergio	9	20

   (a) Who scores the most goals per match?

   (b) Who scores the least goals per match?

2. Alison plays 20 games for her school hockey team and scores 18 goals. Each match lasts 90 minutes.

   Calculate her scoring rate in:

   (a) goals per hour,

   (b) goals per minute,

   (c) goals per match.

3. When playing football, Jai claims to be able, on average, to score a goal every 40 minutes. How many goals would you expect him to score in:

   (a) 90 minutes,

   (b) 1 hour,

   (c) 5 matches,

   (d) 40 matches ?

4. It costs 96p to send an air mail letter of mass 40 grams to Africa, and 107p to send it to China.

   (a) Calculate the cost per gram for each destination.

   (b) If the same rates apply to a 50 gram letter, calculate the cost for each destination.

5. A package of mass 80 grams costs 39p to post first class and 31p to post second class. Calculate the cost per gram for first and second class post.

6. A taxi driver charges £3.20 for a 4 km journey. How much does he charge:

   (a) per km,

   (b) per metre ?

7.   A taxi service makes a fixed charge of £1.20 and then 78p per km.
        Calculate the cost for journeys of the following lengths:

        (a)   1 km   (b)   2 km

        (c)   4.5 km   (d)   10.5 km

8.   Alexi buys a 20 m length of fabric for £18.60.

        (a)   What is the cost per m of the fabric?

        (b)   What would be the cost of 9.2 m of the fabric?

9.   Five people work in a shop. The following table lists the hours worked and
        the total paid in one week:

	Hours Worked	Total Paid
Dee	8	£28.64
Nadina	12	£43.44
Lisa	42	£302.40
Mary	38	£136.80
Clare	35	£134.40

        (a)   Who is paid the *most* per hour?

        (b)   Who is paid the *least* per hour?

10.   A 5 litre tin of paint is used to paint a wall that measures 6.25 m by 4 m.
        Calculate the rate at which paint is applied to the wall, in:

        (a)   litres per m^2,

        (b) cm^3 per m^2,

        (c)   ml per cm^2.

19 Similarity

19.1 Enlargement

An enlargement *increases or decreases* the size of a shape by a multiplier known as the *scale factor*. The *angles* in the shape will *not be changed* by the enlargement.

Example 1

Which of the triangles below are enlargements of the triangle marked A ? State the scale factor of each of these enlargements.

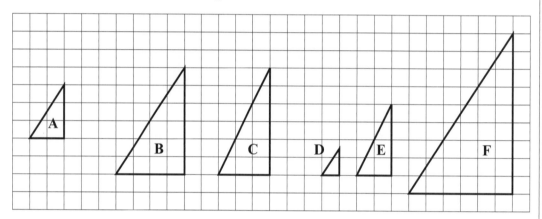

Solution

B is an enlargement of A, since all the lengths are doubled.
The *scale factor* of the enlargement is 2.

C is *not* an enlargement of A.

D is an enlargement of A, since all the lengths are halved.
The *scale factor* of the enlargement is $\frac{1}{2}$.

E is *not* an enlargement of A.

F is an enlargement, since all the lengths are trebled.
The *scale factor* of the enlargement is 3.

Example 2

Ameer has started to draw an enlargement of the quadrilateral marked A. Copy and complete the enlargement.

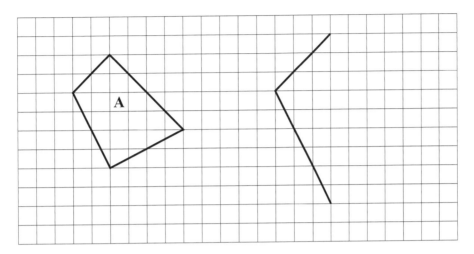

Solution

The diagram shows the completed enlargement.

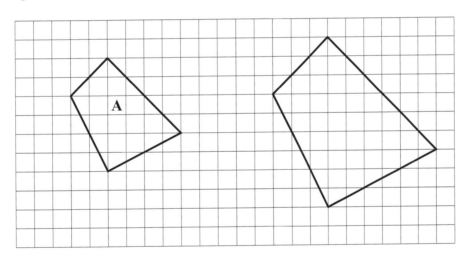

All the lengths have been increased by a factor of $1\frac{1}{2}$.

We say that the *scale factor* of the enlargement is $1\frac{1}{2}$.

Exercises

1. Which of the following shapes are enlargements of shape A ? State the scale factor of each of these enlargements.

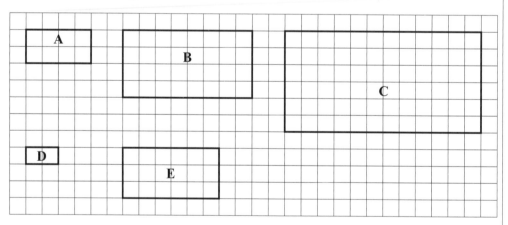

2. Which of the following triangles are *not* enlargements of the triangle marked A ?

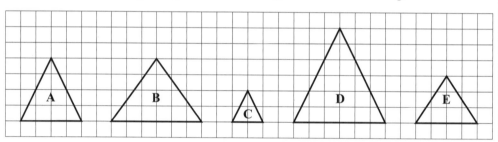

3. The diagram below shows four enlargements of rectangle A. State the scale factor of each enlargement.

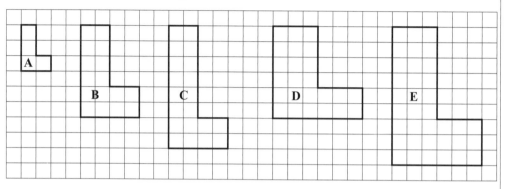

4. Which two signs below are *not* enlargements of sign A ?

5. Which two of the leaves shown below are enlargements of leaf A ?

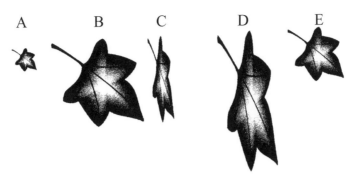

6. Which of the flags below are enlargements of flag A ?

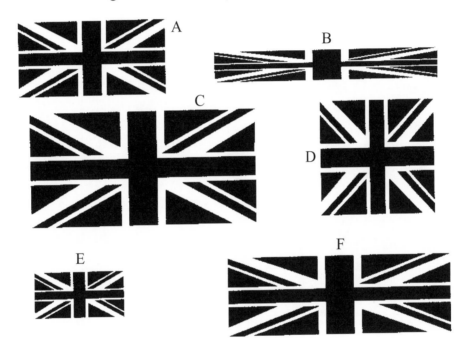

7. Draw enlargements of the rectangle shown
    with scale factors:

    (a)   2   (b)   4

    (c) $\frac{1}{2}$ (d)   3

8. Draw enlargements of the triangle shown
    with scale factors:

    (a)   2

    (b)   3

    (c) $1\frac{1}{2}$

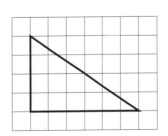

9.   Denise has started to draw an enlargement of the shape below. Copy and complete her enlargement.

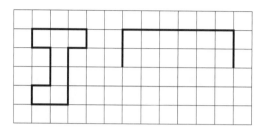

10. Kristian has started to draw an enlargement of the shape below. Copy and complete his enlargement.

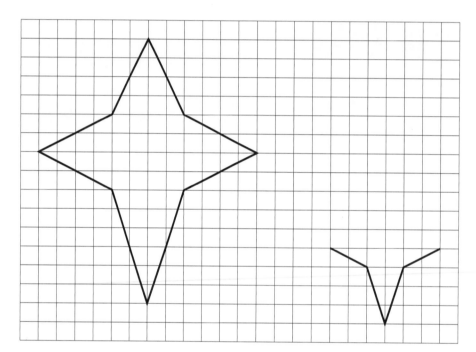

19.2 Similar Shapes

Similar shapes are those which are *enlargements of each other*; for example, the three triangles shown below are similar:

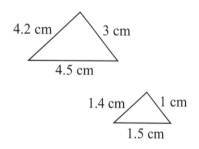

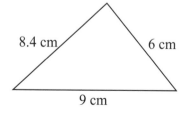

It is possible to calculate the lengths of the sides of similar shapes.

Example 1

The following diagram shows two similar triangles:

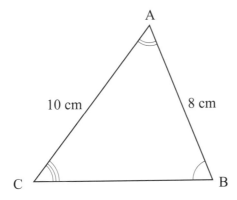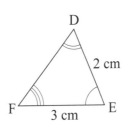

Calculate the lengths of the sides B C and D F.

Solution

Comparing the sides A B and D E gives:

A B = 4 × D E

So, all the lengths in the triangle A B C will be 4 times the lengths of the sides in the triangle D E F.

$$
\begin{aligned}
\text{B C} &= 4 \times \text{E F} \\
&= 4 \times 3 \\
&= 12 \text{ cm}
\end{aligned}
$$

$$
\begin{aligned}
\text{A C} &= 4 \times \text{D F} \\
10 &= 4 \times \text{D F} \\
\text{D F} &= \frac{10}{4} \\
&= 2.5 \text{ cm}
\end{aligned}
$$

Example 2

The following diagram shows 2 similar triangles:

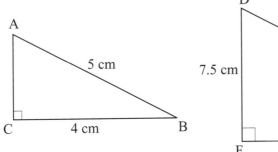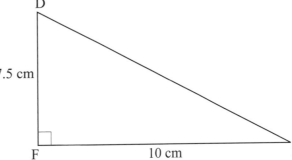

Calculate the lengths of the sides A C and D E.

Solution

Comparing the lengths B C and E F gives:

$$E F = 2.5 \times B C$$

So the lengths in the triangle D E F are 2.5 times longer than the lengths in the triangle A B C.

$$
\begin{aligned}
D E &= 2.5 \times A B \\
&= 2.5 \times 5 \\
&= 12.5 \text{ cm}
\end{aligned}
$$

$$
\begin{aligned}
D F &= 2.5 \times A C \\
7.5 &= 2.5 \times A C \\
A C &= \frac{7.5}{2.5} \\
&= 3 \text{ cm}
\end{aligned}
$$

Example 3

In the following diagram, the sides A E and B C are parallel.

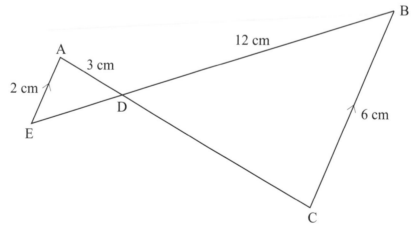

(a)   Explain why A D E and C D B are similar triangles.

(b)   Calculate the lengths D E and C D.

Solution

(a) $\angle$ A D E and $\angle$ C D B are opposite angles and so are equal.

Because A E and B C are parallel, $\angle$ D B C = $\angle$ D E A and $\angle$ E A D = $\angle$ B C D.

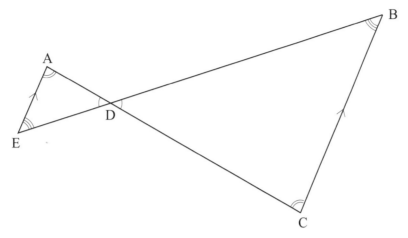

As the triangles have angles the same size, they must be similar.

(b) Comparing A E and B C shows that the lengths in the larger triangle are 3 times the lengths of the sides in the smaller triangle, so

$$D C = 3 \times A D$$
$$= 3 \times 3$$
$$= 9 \text{ cm}$$

and

$$B D = 3 \times D E$$
$$12 = 3 \times D E$$
$$D E = \frac{12}{3}$$
$$= 4 \text{ cm}$$

Exercises

1. The following diagram shows two similar rectangles:

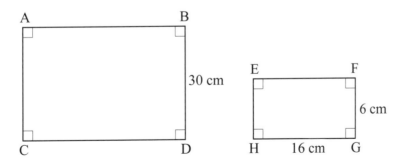

Determine the length of the side C D.

2.   The following diagram shows two similar triangles:

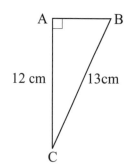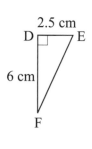

Calculate the lengths of:

(a)   A B   (b)   E F

3.   Two similar isosceles triangles are shown in the diagram below:

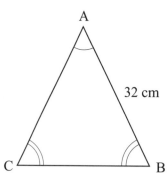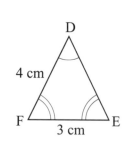

(a)   What is the length of D E ?

(b)   What is the length of A C ?

(c)   Calculate the length of B C.

4.   The following diagram shows two similar triangles:

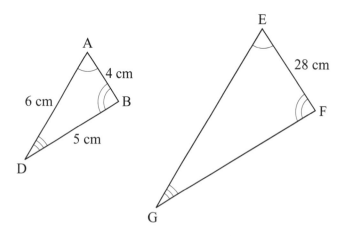

Calculate the lengths of the sides G E and F G.

5.   The following diagram shows three similar triangles:

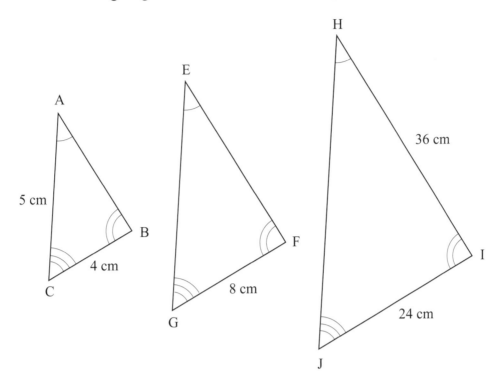

Calculate the length of:

(a)   E G

(b)   H J

(c)   E F

(d)   A B

6.   The following diagram shows 3 similar triangles:

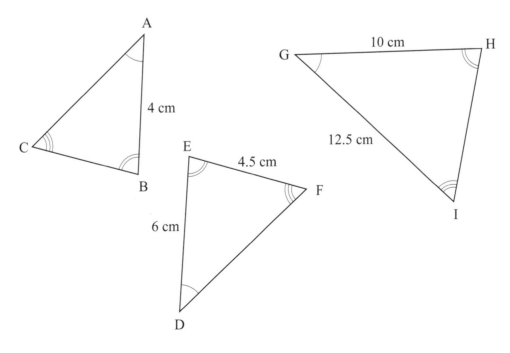

Calculate the length of the sides:

(a)   H I

(b)   B C

(c)   A C

(d)   D F

7.   The following diagram shows two similar shapes:

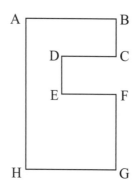 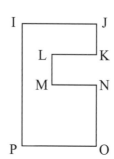

The length of the side A B is 6 cm and the length of the side I J is 4 cm.

(a)   If A H = 12 cm, calculate the length I P.

(b)   If B C = 3 cm, calculate the length J K.

(c)   If D E = B C, determine the length L M.

(d)   Calculate the lengths F G and N O.

(e)   If M N = 3 cm, determine the length E F.

8.   In the diagram below, the lines A E and C D are parallel.

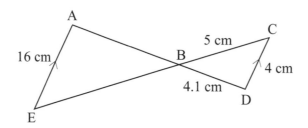

(a)   Copy and complete the following statements:

∠ A B E = ∠

∠ B A E = ∠

∠ A E B = ∠

(b)   Calculate the lengths of A B and B E.

9. In the diagram shown below the lines B E and C D are parallel.

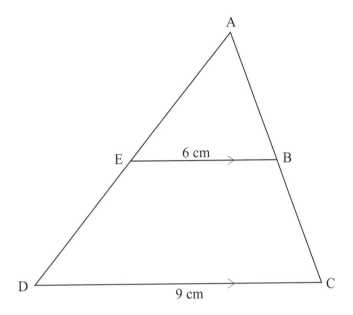

(a) Explain why the triangles A B E and A C D are similar.

(b) If the length of A B is 4.4 cm, calculate the lengths of A C and B C.

(c) If the length of A D is 13.5 cm, determine the lengths of A E and D E.

10. In the diagram shown, the lines A B, G D and F E are parallel.

    (a) If the length of C E is 15 cm, calculate the lengths of A C, C D and D E.

    (b) If the length of B C is 10.8 cm, calculate the length of F G.

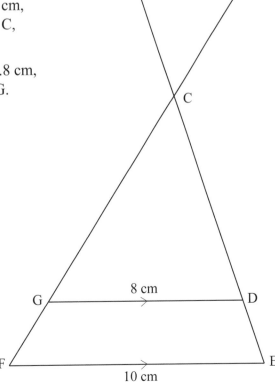

19.3 Line, Area and Volume Ratios

In this section we consider what happens to the area and volume of shapes when they are enlarged.

Example 1

The rectangle shown is enlarged with scale factor 2 and scale factor 3.

What happens to the *area* for each scale factor?

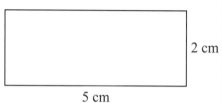

5 cm

2 cm

Solution

The area of the original rectangle is

area = 5×2

     = 10 cm^2

For an enlargement scale factor 2, the rectangle becomes:

area = 10×4

     = 40 cm^2

The area has increased by a factor of 4, or 2^2.

10 cm

4 cm

For an enlargement scale factor 3, the rectangle becomes:

area = 15×6

     = 90 cm^2

15 cm

6 cm

The area has increased by a factor of 9, or 3^2.

Note

If a shape is enlarged with scale factor k,

its area is increased by a factor k^2.

Example 2

A hexagon has area 60 cm^2 .

Calculate the area of the hexagon, if it is enlarged with scale factor:

(a) 2   (b) 4   (c) 10

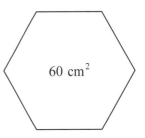

60 cm^2

Solution

In each case the area will increase by the scale factor squared.

(a) New area $=$ $2^2 \times 60$

$=$ 4×60

$=$ 240 cm^2

(b) New area $=$ $4^2 \times 60$

$=$ 16×60

$=$ 960 cm^2

(c) New area $=$ $10^2 \times 60$

$=$ 100×60

$=$ 6000 cm^2

Example 3

A cuboid has sides of lengths 3 cm, 4 cm and 5 cm.

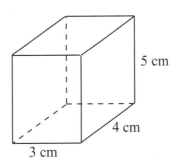

5 cm

4 cm

3 cm

Calculate the volume of the cuboid, if it is enlarged with scale factor:

(a) 2   (b) 10

Solution

(a) The dimensions of the cuboid now become,

6 cm, 8 cm and 10 cm.

New volume $= 6 \times 8 \times 10$

$\qquad = 480 \ \text{cm}^3$

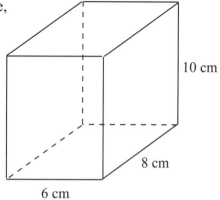

Note that the volume of the original cuboid was $60 \ \text{cm}^3$, so the volume has increased by a factor of 8, or 2^3.

(b) The dimensions of the cuboid now become,

30 cm, 40 cm and 50 cm.

New volume $= 30 \times 40 \times 50$

$\qquad = 60 \ 000 \ \text{cm}^3$

Note that this is 1000, or 10^3, times bigger than the volume of the original cuboid.

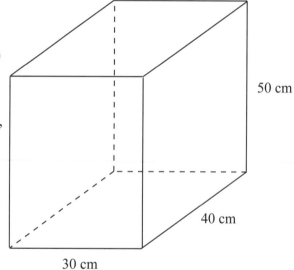

> *Note*
> If a solid is enlarged with scale factor k,
> its volume is increased by a factor k^3.

Example 4

A sphere has a volume of 20 cm^3. A second sphere has 4 times the radius of the first sphere. Calculate the volume of the second sphere.

Solution

The radius is increased by a factor of 4.

The volume will be increased by a factor of 4^3.

$$
\begin{aligned}
\text{Volume} \ &= \ 20 \times 4^3 \\
&= \ 20 \times 64 \\
&= \ 1280 \text{ cm}^3
\end{aligned}
$$

Exercises

1. Two rectangles are shown below:

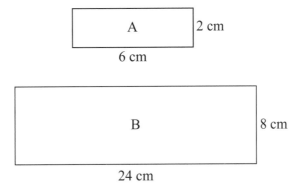

   (a) Calculate the area of each rectangle.

   (b) How many times longer are the sides in rectangle B than those in rectangle A ?

   (c) How many times bigger is the area of rectangle B ?

2. Calculate the area of the rectangle shown if it is enlarged with a scale factor of:

   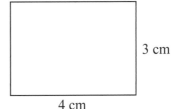

   (a) 2   (b) 3

   (c) 6   (d) 10

3.   The following table gives information about
      enlargements of the triangle shown, which
      has an area of 6 cm².

      Copy and complete the table.

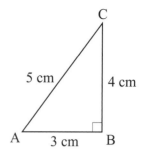

| Length of Sides | | Scale Factor | Area | Area Factor |
Base	Height			
3 cm	4 cm	1	6 cm²	1
		2		
	12 cm			
	16 cm			
15 cm				
		6		
30 cm	40 cm		600 cm²	100
4.5 cm				

4.   The parallelogram shown has an area of 42 cm².

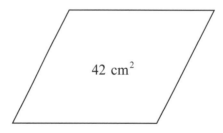

42 cm²

      The parallelogram is enlarged with a scale factor of 5.

      Calculate the area of the enlarged parallelogram.

5.   The area of a circle is 50 cm². A second circle has a radius that is 3 times
      the radius of the first circle. What is the area of this circle?

6.   Two similar rectangles have areas of 30 cm² and 480 cm². Describe how
      the length and width of the two rectangles compare.

7. (a) Determine the volume of each of the following cuboids:

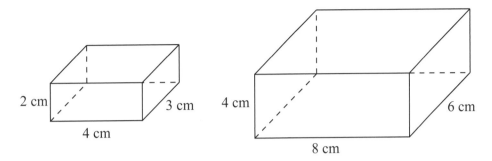

2 cm   3 cm   4 cm   4 cm   6 cm   8 cm

(b) The larger cuboid is an enlargement of the smaller cuboid. What is the scale factor of the enlargement?

(c) How many of the smaller cuboids can be fitted into the larger cuboid?

(d) How many times greater is the volume of the larger cuboid than the volume of the smaller cuboid?

8. A cuboid has dimensions as shown in the diagram.

The cuboid is enlarged to give larger cuboids. Copy and complete the following table:

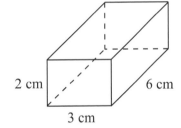

2 cm   6 cm   3 cm

Dimensions			Scale Factor	Volume	Volume Factor
Width	Length	Height			
3 cm	6 cm	2 cm	1	36 cm³	1
6 cm			2		
			4		
		10 cm			
30 cm					

9. A tank has a volume of 32 m³. It is enlarged with scale factor 3. What is the volume of the enlarged tank?

10. A cylinder has height 10 cm and volume 42 cm³. An enlargement of the cylinder has height 25 cm. Calculate the volume of the enlarged cylinder.

19.4 Maps and Scale Models

The ideas of how areas and volumes change with enlargement were considered in section 19.3. Here we apply these ideas to maps and scale models.

> If a map has a scale $1 : n,$ then:
>   lengths have a scale of $1 : n$
>   and areas have a scale of $1 : n^2$.
>
> If a model has a scale of $1 : n,$ then
>   lengths have a scale of $1 : n$
>   areas have a scale of $1 : n^2$
>   and volumes have a scale of $1 : n^3$.

> *Note on units*
>
> $1 \text{ km} = 1000 \text{ m}$
> $= 100\,000 \text{ cm}$
> $1 \text{ m}^2 = 10\,000 \text{ cm}^2$
> $1 \text{ m}^3 = 1\,000\,000 \text{ cm}^3$

Example 1

On a map with a scale of $1 : 20\,000,$ a garden has an area of 5 cm^2. Calculate the actual area of the garden.

Solution

$$\begin{aligned}
\text{Actual area} &= 5 \times 20\,000^2 \\
&= 2\,000\,000\,000 \text{ cm}^2 \\
&= 200\,000 \text{ m}^2 \text{ (dividing by 10 000)} \\
&= 0.2 \text{ km}^2 \quad \text{(dividing by 1 000 000)}
\end{aligned}$$

Example 2

A map has a scale of $1 : 500.$ A small public garden on the map has an area of 14 cm^2. Calculate the actual area of this garden.

Solution

$$\begin{aligned}
\text{Actual area} &= 14 \times 500^2 \\
&= 3\,500\,000 \text{ cm}^2 \\
&= 350 \text{ m}^2
\end{aligned}$$

Example 3

A model car is made on a scale of 1 : 20.

The length of the model is 24 cm.

The area of the windscreen of the model is 32 cm^2.

The volume of the boot of the model is 90 cm^3.

Calculate the actual:

(a)   length of the car,

(b)   area of the windscreen,

(c)   volume of the boot.

Solution

(a)   Actual length $=$ 24×20

$=$ 480 cm

$=$ 4.8 m

(b)   Actual area $=$ 32×20^2

$=$ 12800 cm^2

$=$ 1.28 m^2

(c)   Actual volume $=$ 90×20^3

$=$ 720000 cm^3

$=$ 0.72 m^3

Exercises

1.   A model boat is made to a scale of 1 : 10.
    The length of the model is 40 cm.
    The area of the hull of the model is 500 cm^2.
    The volume of the hull of the model is 3200 cm^3.

    Calculate the actual:

    (a)   length of the boat,

    (b)   area of the hull,

    (c)   volume of the hull.

2. A map has a scale of 1 : 50 000. On the map the area of a lake is 50 cm^2.
    Calculate the actual area of the lake in:

    (a)   cm^2 (b)   m^2 (c)   km^2

3. A model of a tower block is made with a scale of 1 : 60. The volume of the
    model is 36 000 cm^3. Calculate the volume of the actual tower block in m^3.

4. A plot of land is represented on a map by a rectangle 2 cm by 5 cm. The
    scale of the map is 1 : 40 000. Calculate the area of the plot of land in:

    (a)   cm^2 (b)   m^2 (c)   km^2

5. A model of a house is made to a scale of 1 : 30.

    The height of the model is 20 cm.

    The area of the roof of the model is 850 cm^2.

    The volume of the model house of 144 400 cm^3.

    Calculate the actual:

    (a)   height of the house in m,

    (b)   area of the roof in m^2,

    (c)   volume of the house in m^3.

6. An aeroplane has a wingspan of 12 m. A model of this plane has a
    wingspan of 60 cm.

    (a)   Calculate the scale of the model.

    (b)   The volume of the model is 3015 cm^3. Calculate the volume of the
          actual aeroplane, in m^3.

    (c)   A badge on the model has area 2 cm^2. Calculate the area of the actual
          badge, in cm^2 and m^2.

7. A forest has an area of 4 cm^2 on a map with a scale of 1 : 200 000.
    Calculate the actual area of the forest, in km^2.

8. An estate has an area of 50 km^2. What would be the area of the estate on a
    map with a scale of 1 : 40 000 ?

9.   An indoor sports stadium has 5000 seats surrounding a playing area with an area of 384 m^2. The total volume of the stadium is 3840 m^3. A model is made to a scale of $1 : 80$.

   (a)   How many seats are there in the model?

   (b)   What is the area of the playing surface in the model, in cm^2 ?

   (c)   What is the volume of the model, in cm^3 ?

10.   A lake has an area of 5 km^2. On a map it is represented by an area of 20 cm^2. What is the scale of the map?

20 Questionnaires and Analysis

20.1 Questionnaire Design

Questionnaires must be designed carefully so that the answers given produce the required information: they should do so without influencing the people completing them. The following list contains points to consider when designing a questionnaire:

The questions should be worded to provide the information needed by the researcher.

Care must be taken not to invade people's privacy, so questions that do not relate to the purpose of the questionnaire must be excluded.

The questions should be capable of being answered reasonably quickly.

The questions should be easy to understand and should not be ambiguous.

The questionnaire should not contain biased or leading questions.

Questions may have possible responses presented in a multiple choice, or YES/NO format.

Where responses are provided, they should cover every possible answer.

The responses provided should not overlap.

The responses provided should not force people to answer in a way that they do not wish to answer.

The questionnaire should be designed so that the results are easy to analyse.

You should try out a questionnaire in a pilot study of a few people before using it with a large group of people. This will allow you the opportunity to alter questions that do not work well; for example, where they are misinterpreted.

Example 1

Aisha wants to identify the favourite colours of children of different ages. Comment on the following questions that she has decided to ask:

1. *Which age range are you in?*

   0 - 5 ☐

   6 - 12 ☐

   12 + ☐

2. *Please tick the colour that you like most from this list:*

   Blue ☐

   Green ☐

   Yellow ☐

   Orange ☐

   Black ☐

Solution

- The questionnaire is easy to fill in and the data will be easy to collect and analyse.

- An adult could answer question 1 and you would not be aware of this, as the 12 + category would include children and adults.

- The age categories overlap. A 12-year old would not know whether to tick the second or third box.

- The survey only asks for the preferred colour from a limited choice. If you want to find the *favourite* colour, you will have to give many more choices (red and purple, for example, are colours which people might want to choose as their favourites).

- An alternative way of improving the second question would be to have an extra category labelled

  'Other colour (please specify) ☐ . . . . '

Example 2

Comment on the questions below:

1.   *Do cars cause pollution in the city centre?*   YES ☐
                                                            NO   ☐

2.   *Do cars cause traffic hold-ups in the city centre?* YES ☐
                                                            NO   ☐

3.   *Are some car drivers a danger to pedestrians in the city centre?* YES ☐
                                                            NO   ☐

4.   *Do you think that cars should be banned from the city centre?* YES ☐
                                                            NO   ☐

Solution

The questions are biased. The first three are designed to focus on the disadvantages and dangers of cars, so that people are more likely to say 'yes' when they answer question 4.

Exercises

1.   Design a questionnaire to find out whether people would be in favour of banning cars from your nearest city centre.

2.   Design a questionnaire that could be used to investigate students' opinions of the method of transport that they use to travel to school.

3.   Design a questionnaire to investigate how students rate the quality of the meals served in your school canteen.

4.   Design a questionnaire that can be used to determine whether the general public, in your area, would be in favour of building a new youth club.

5.   Rewrite the following questions so that they are not biased in any way:

     (a)   Do you agree that maths is boring?

     (b)   Are you in favour of town centre car park charges being increased in order to discourage car drivers from using their cars?

     (c)   The price of a school lunch has not increased for 2 years. Do you think that school lunches are good value for money?

6. Comment critically on the following questions. In each case, rewrite the question to show the improvements you have made.

    (a) *Are you young, middle-aged or old?*

    (b) *Please select your favourite breakfast cereal from this list:*

    Cornflakes ☐   Rice Crispies ☐

    Frosties ☐   Bran Flakes ☐

    (c) *How old are you?*

    $0 \rightarrow 5$ ☐

    $7 \rightarrow 10$ ☐

    $12 +$ ☐

    (d) *Do you have any brothers?*

    Do you have one brother?

    Do you have more than one brother?

    Do you have at least two brothers?

7. Design biased questionnaires that would encourage people to reach the conclusion that the government:

    (a) dislikes motorists,

    (b) encourages motorists.

8. The local council interviews people who are arriving in the city centre on a warm, sunny day. People are asked which of the following methods of transport they have used:

    Walking ☐   Cycling ☐

    Bus ☐   Car ☐

    (a) Explain why the results may not be reliable for deciding transport policies.

    (b) Suggest how the council should collect more data.

9. As part of a survey, children were asked on which days they watched television during the previous week.

    (a) Describe what problems the researchers may have had in reporting on how much television these children watched.

    (b) Design a better question or questions to gather data for a report on how much television children watch.

10. Design a questionnaire that could be used to gather data on how school children spend their summer holidays.

20.2 Data Display

In this section we revise how to display data visually using *bar charts, vertical line diagrams, pie charts* and *pictograms*.

Example 1

At the end of each half term, the students in a particular school are graded A, B or C for their reports. The table shows the grades awarded for one class.

Illustrate this data using a *pie chart*.

Grade	Frequency
A	12
B	16
C	2

Solution

The angles must be calculated first:

Grade	Frequency	Angle
A	12	$\frac{12}{30} \times 360\,° = 144\,°$
B	16	$\frac{16}{30} \times 360\,° = 192\,°$
C	2	$\frac{2}{30} \times 360\,° = 24\,°$
TOTALS	30	$360\,°$

The pie chart can then be drawn as shown below:

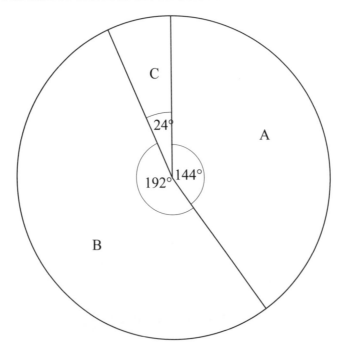

Both the table and the pie chart show that very few of the pupils in this class were awarded a poor grade (C), and that B was the grade most frequently awarded to this class.

Example 2

A school canteen offers students a choice of burgers, sandwiches, baked potatoes or the meal of the day. On one day the number of children making each choice was recorded; the table below shows the children's choices for that day.

Choice	Frequency
Sandwiches	160
Burgers	45
Baked Potatoes	90
Meal of the Day	225

Illustrate this data using:

(a)   a *pictogram*,

(b)   a *bar chart*.

Solution

(a)   *Pictogram to Show the Choices Made in a School Canteen*

Sandwiches	🧍🧍🧍🧍🧍🧍🧍🧍🧍🧍🧍🧍🧍🧍🧍🧍
Burgers	🧍🧍🧍🧍🧍
Baked Potatoes	🧍🧍🧍🧍🧍🧍🧍🧍🧍
Meal of the Day	🧍🧍🧍🧍🧍🧍🧍🧍🧍🧍🧍🧍🧍🧍🧍🧍🧍🧍🧍🧍🧍🧍

🧍 = 10 people

(b)   *Bar Chart to Show the Choices Made in a School Canteen*

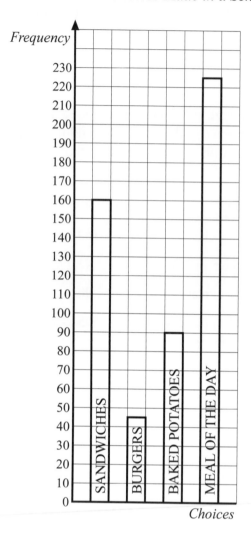

Example 3

The pupils in class 7C were given a short maths test. The scores are listed in the following table:

Score	0	1	2	3	4	5	6	7	8	9	10
Frequency	0	2	3	2	5	3	7	6	3	0	2

Illustrate these results on a *vertical line diagram*.

Solution

Vertical Line Diagram to Show the Results of a Maths Test for Pupils in Class 7C

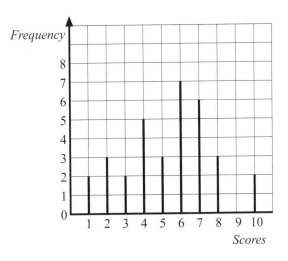

Exercises

1. Ameer visits a car park and records the registration letter of each of the cars there. The results are given in the table below:

Letter	P	R	S	T	V	W	OTHER
Frequency	3	6	7	2	5	3	10

Illustrate Ameer's data using a pie chart.

2. Pupils in class 8B record the number of bus journeys made by each member of their class during one week. The results are listed in the following table:

No. of Journeys	0	1	2	3	4	5	6	7	8	9	10	11	12	13	14
Frequency	6	2	1	0	0	0	0	1	1	1	14	2	1	0	1

(a) Illustrate this data using a *vertical line diagram*.

(b) Give a possible reason why the category '10 journeys' has such a high frequency.

3.   A survey was carried out to see how children in a school rated their school bus service. The results are listed in the following table:

Response	Frequency
Very good	1
Good	7
Satisfactory	26
Bad	24
Very bad	2

Illustrate these results with a *pictogram*. Write a brief note to the bus company commenting on what the survey shows about the quality of the service they provide to the school

4.   Mandy draws the following bar chart to illustrate the ages of some of her friends:

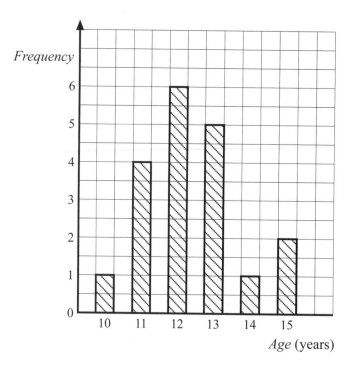

(a)   How many of Mandy's friends are included on the bar chart?

(b)   Mandy is 13 years old. How many of her friends are the same age as she is?

(c)   How many of her friends are aged 14 or younger?

5.   A class carried out a survey to find out how many TV sets there were in each of their homes. The results are shown in the following table:

Number of TV Sets	0	1	2	3	4	5
Frequency	1	8	14	2	3	1

Illustrate this data using a *bar chart,* and comment on the results of the survey.

6.   Jason has £3 per week pocket money. One week, Jason spent his £3 pocket money on the following items:

Sweets	60p
Football club	£1.00
Tennis club	50p
Comics	70p
New pencil	20p

(a)   Explain why a pie chart would be a good way to show how Jason spent his pocket money that week.

(b)   Draw a pie chart to show how Jason spent that week's pocket money.

7.   The pupils in a class carry out a survey to determine their favourite types of television programme. The results are given in the following table:

Soaps	8
Films	9
News programmes	1
Quizzes	2
Wildlife programmes	4
Others	6

(a)   Illustrate this data using a suitable diagram.

(b)   Explain why you chose to illustrate the data using this method.

8. A pocket money survey for a group of 50 students produced the following results:

Weekly Pocket Money	£1	£2	£3	£5	£10
Frequency	10	22	12	5	1

(a) Illustrate this data using a suitable diagram.

(b) Explain why you chose this type of diagram to illustrate the data.

(c) Sam gets £4 pocket money each week. Would Sam be wise to use the results of this survey to support his request for an increase in his pocket money?

9. (a) Carry out a survey to find the favourite type of chocolate bar for your class.

(b) Illustrate your results with a suitable diagram.

(c) Comment on your results.

10. (a) Collect data on the age, in years and months, of each member of your class.

(b) Illustrate the data with a suitable diagram.

(c) Comment on the results you obtain.

20.3 Line Graphs

In this section we look at how to use line graphs.

Example 1

Mr Smith recorded the temperature outside his classroom every hour during one school day. His results are listed in the following table:

Time	0900	1000	1100	1200	1300	1400	1500	1600
Temperature (°C)	8	9	11	12	12	13	10	9

(a) Plot this data using a line graph.

(b) Estimate the temperature at 1030 and at 1130.

Solution

(a)   First plot the points that represent each of the recorded temperatures and then join these points with straight lines, as shown in the following diagram:

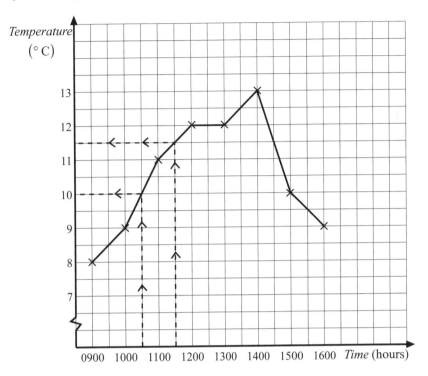

(b)   The broken lines added to the graph show how to estimate the temperature at other times. The estimate for the temperature at

1030 is 10 °   and at   1130 is 11.5 °

Example 2

The following line graph shows how much rain had fallen by certain times one day:

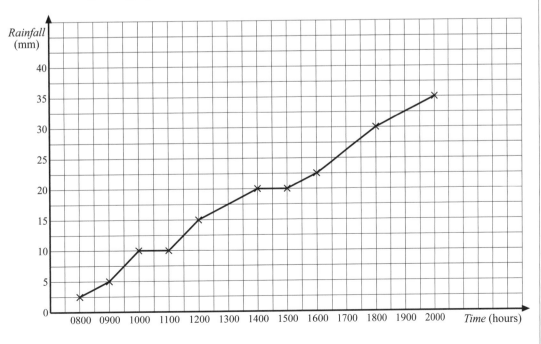

Estimate the amount of rain that had fallen by:

(a)   1030   (b)   1300

(c)   1900   (d)   between 1300 and 1900

During which times did *no* rain fall?

Solution

The broken lines on the following graph show how to obtain the estimates:

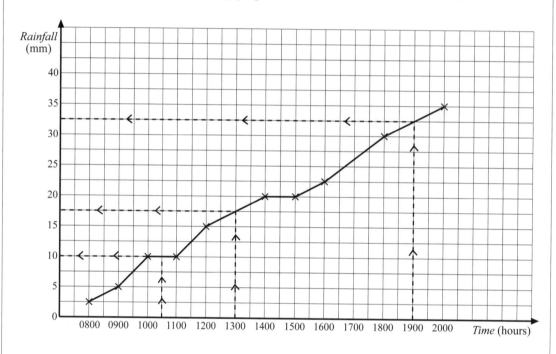

Estimates: (a)   By 1030, 10 mm of rain had fallen.

(b)   By 1300, 17.5 mm of rain had fallen.

(c)   By 1900, 32.5 mm of rain had fallen.

(d)   This means that approximately $32.5 - 17.5 = 15$ mm of rain fell between 1300 and 1900.

The horizontal sections of the graph indicate that it did not rain at all between 1000 and 1100 and also between 1400 and 1500. (There may have been other *short* periods of time when it did not rain.)

Exercises

1. The outside temperature was recorded every hour during a school day. The results are given below:

Time	0900	1000	1100	1200	1300	1400	1500	1600
Temperature ($^\circ$ C)	12	13	16	18	22	21	20	18

(a) Draw a line graph for this data.

(b) Estimate the temperature at 1230 and at 1530.

2. The height of a plant was measured regularly after it had been transplanted, and the results are given below:

Day	4	8	12	16	20	24
Height (cm)	2	3	6	10	12	14

(a) Draw a line graph to show how the height of the plant increased.

(b) Estimate the height of the plant after:

   (i)   10 days   (ii)   18 days   (iii)   13 days

3. A motorist on a long journey recorded the distances that he had travelled by various times:

Time	0800	0900	1000	1100	1200	1400
Distance Travelled (miles)	0	60	100	150	210	320

(a) Draw a line graph for this data.

(b) Estimate the distance travelled at:

   (i)   0830   (ii)   1130   (iii)   1300

4. Rachel keeps a record of the mass of her puppy as it grows. The records she has gathered are listed below:

Age of Puppy (months)	1	2	4	6	9	10	12
Mass (kg)	5	8	11	12	20	23	24

Use a line graph to estimate the mass of the puppy when its age is:

(a) 3 months

(b) 8 months,

(c) 11 months.

5.   During a flood alert the depth of water in a river was measured several times. The times and depths were recorded as shown below:

Time	0700	0900	1200	1600	2000	2200	2400
Depth (m)	1.4	1.8	1.9	2.2	2.6	3.0	2.8

Use a line graph to estimate the depth of the river at:

(a)   1000   (b)   1800   (c)   2300

6.   The depth of water in a harbour was recorded at various times during one day. The data recorded is listed below:

Time	0600	0900	1000	1200	1600	1800	2000	2400
Depth (m)	3	1.8	1.2	0.8	2.1	3.2	2.4	1.9

Use a line graph to estimate the depth of water in the harbour at:

(a)   0800   (b)   1400   (c)   2200

7.   The following table shows records of a patient's temperature while she was in hospital:

Day	Wednesday				Thursday				Friday
Time	0600	1200	1800	2400	0600	1200	1800	2400	0600
Temperature ($^\circ$C)	38.7	39.1	39.4	39.8	40	39.2	38.4	37.4	37

Use a line graph to estimate when the patient's temperature:

(a)   rose above $39.5\,^\circ$C,

(b)   fell below $38\,^\circ$C.

8.   In a science experiment, masses are hung on the end of a spring and the length of the spring is measured. The results are recorded in the following table:

Mass (gms)	50	100	200	400
Length (cm)	5.6	6.3	7.7	10.5

Use a line graph to estimate the length of the spring for:

(a)   a 150 gram mass   (b)   a 300 gram mass   (c)   a 500 gram mass.

9. The table opposite lists the increase in the average temperature of the earth since 1800.

Year	Temperature Increase (°C)
1860	0.03
1920	0.06
1940	0.10
1960	0.18
1980	0.32
2000	0.60

Use a line graph to estimate the temperature increase by the year:

(a) 1950   (b) 1990   (c) 2020

10. Julie goes on a 5 week diet. She records her mass every 5 days.

Day	0	5	10	15	20	25	30	35
Mass (kg)	74	73	71	68	68	68	67	64

Use a line graph to determine when Julie's mass dropped to:

(a) 72 kg   (b) 70 kg   (c) 65 kg